Man and Animal

Edited by Heinz Friedrich
Translated from the German by Mechthild Nawiasky

Man and Animal
Studies in Behaviour

Hansjochem Autrum   Erich von Holst

Sven Dijkgraaf   Otto Koehler

Karl von Frisch   Konrad Lorenz

Bernhard Grzimek   N. Tinbergen

St. Martin's Press   New York

AFFILIATED PUBLISHERS: Macmillan & Company, Limited,
London – also at Bombay, Calcutta, Madras and Melbourne –
The Macmillan Company of Canada, Limited, Toronto

Contents

CONTENTS

List of Figures

Preface

It is almost everywhere de rigueur in well educated circles today to be able to talk intelligently about the comparative behaviour of animals and man. Books on the subject, some of them best-sellers, have proliferated as fast as mushrooms in the field.

Ten or so years ago such books would have attracted only a very limited readership. The most carefully worded references to comparative treatment of human and animal behaviour would then still have been received with condescension and scepticism by most intellectuals, who would have had such a thorough-going prejudice against, or ignorance of, biology as to preclude any interest in the subject whatsoever. It was simply not done to put *Homo sapiens*, distinguished by the primacy of his spiritual genius, on a level with animals, and to reduce his responses, his emotions and insights, to the mere working out of laws of nature, suddenly supposed to be valid for man as well as for the higher animals.

The change in attitudes during the last decade and a half towards research in comparative behaviour seems all the more surprising. Although the facts which have been discovered by animal psychologists as a result of their studies and experiments are by no means more comfortable to contemplate now than they were before, research into animal behaviour, or 'ethology', has advanced to become a leading international science, just as sociology earlier moved into the limelight as a fashionable subject for research, and one whose progress has still by no means reached its climax. But these developments do not appear so strange when one remembers that anthropological science, which has its origins in the idealistic humanism of the nineteenth century, was quite inadequately equipped for the new human realities of the twentieth century.

Even sociology, which has advanced furthest into the territory of pure science from its own base in the humanities, reached its limits when it was required to define the ultimate origins of certain social phenomena. If sociologists were not to get bogged down in vague speculations and hypotheses, they had no choice but to consult their colleagues in the departments of natural history who had long ago discovered that man, so idealistically and grandly styled as the sole bearer of the true, the good and the beautiful, was in fact far from being the unique being he had so fondly thought he was. They had also discovered that the much esteemed human 'free will' was not as effective as had been supposed, as certain striking actions of *Homo sapiens* proved. On the contrary, the well founded suspicion arose that human will alone cannot help man to escape from certain basic patterns on which nature has shaped his very existence, even in those spheres where he hopes to be free from predetermined organic patterns of existence. Konrad Lorenz produced cogent instances of this in his epoch-making work on aggression.

But on the other hand, natural scientists have been criticised for their tendency to confine humanity within the bounds of a materialistic and mechanical outlook on psycho-biological problems. Ethological research in particular has been said to reduce anthropological questions to physical content only, thus excluding the metaphysical side of life without which humanity loses its greatness. Yet natural scientists have seldom undertaken to join battle with metaphysicians, still less to encroach on their preserves (those like Haeckel or Ostwald who have been guilty of trespassing have hardly helped themselves or their discipline); they have simply attempted to delimit the basic realities with which natural science deals, thus providing metaphysical enquiry with some safeguard from transcendental illusions and speculative culs-de-sacs. To enquire into man's real nature requires coming to terms with the basic physiological ingredients of *Homo sapiens*, because the spirit is intrinsically bound up with the functions of the body. The dualistic view of human existence is still widely held, but fights a rearguard action in the light of the countless facts increasingly marshalled by science that point decisively towards a unity of living processes. Such facts have long been intuitively grasped by enlightened minds from Heraclitus to Nietzsche. Modern cybernetics, clarifying information processes, has contributed its conclusive demonstration of the coordinated action of sensory perception per se and bodily responses, involving evaluation and transformation of what is perceived. Without directive intelligence – which is active in some degree even in minute single-cell organisms – organisms disintegrate into an amorphous mass, lose their unity by dying, and liberate their particles for incorporation into new organisms. But intelligence cannot exist in a void, without physical organs. The cooperation of mind and body, of energy and matter, has to occur for life to originate and persist. Einstein's genius formulated these three factors together as the basic law of our universe as simply and concisely as this: $e = mc^2$ (energy equals matter multiplied by the square of the speed of light). If this formula is correct (and there is overwhelming evidence of the likelihood that it is), it would be folly to ignore the consequences which arise from it – such as that life patterns generated in accordance with the formula always recur in different variations and thus determine the modes of behaviour of all creatures, but that, within certain limits, some self-determined developments are possible.

Inspired by such vistas, ethologists, observing and comparing the patterns of behaviour of many different species of animals, provided some understanding of the workings of the 'world-image apparatus' of living organisms (to use Konrad Lorenz's term). The importance of distinguishing between inherited and acquired characteristics became clear. The so-called 'releasing mechanisms' were discovered, which are largely responsible for the characteristic behaviour of all individual members of a species and are independent of individual intentions. To name only a few among today's eminent ethologists, Otto Koehler discovered the phenomenon of 'non-verbal thinking', Konrad Lorenz illuminated that of *Gestaltwahrnehmung* (Gestalt perception) and aggression, and N. Tinbergen analysed the social behaviour of animals. Scientists such as these arrived at far-reaching conclusions which stimulated further investigations, comparisons and analogies with human behaviour. Explanations were suddenly found for many seemingly incongruous facts which had previously eluded logical classification by anthropologists because, to borrow a term used in cybernetics, the 'programme' determining certain modes of behaviour was unknown.

The decoding of the secrets of human conduct is increasingly accelerated by the fascinating and still relatively young discipline of ethology, a branch of zoology which has moved into a central position between the natural sciences and the humanities, between physics and metaphysics. The horizons of the natural sciences were widened considerably when the old positivist-pragmatic yardsticks were abandoned. Humanists now have to accept more biology than of old before meditating on or beyond man's earthly existence. One hopes that future generations – not only of scientists – will be grateful for the results of ethological research.

The majority of the contributions by leading ethologists published here together were originally written for radio in the early fifties, but none has lost its topical or informative value – rather the opposite.

My grateful thanks are due to the authors for their kind agreement to having their papers presented to a wider and better informed public than two decades ago. All the authors have corrected and amplified their work for this edition. Professor Koehler has gone to considerable trouble to rewrite completely his contribution 'Prototypes of Human Communication Systems in Animals'. The editor wishes to express his particular gratitude for this mark of distinction conferred on his project. Thanks are also due to Mr Hermann Kacher whose drawings of ravens richly illustrate the article by Professor Lorenz; and to Verlag Alfred Kröner, Stuttgart, who kindly allowed the editor to reprint the texts.

Heinz Friedrich

PUBLISHER'S NOTE ON THE ENGLISH EDITION

References to the journal *Zeitschrift für Tierpsychologie* in the text of the original German edition of this book (*Mensch und Tier*, Deutscher Taschenbuch Verlag, Munich, 1968) are excluded from the present edition.

Professor Tinbergen's essay included in the German edition under the title 'Über Kampf und Drohen im Tierreich' is here replaced by the text (slightly edited) of his inaugural lecture as Professor of Animal Behaviour at the University of Oxford, as published in *Science*, Vol. 160, pp. 1411–1418, 28 June 1968. Grateful acknowledgment is made to Professor Tinbergen and to the American Association for the Advancement of Science for their kind permission to reprint this copyright material.

Publishers and translator wish to thank Sir Gavin de Beer and Dr R. D. Martin of the Department of Anthropology, University College, London for the benefit of their kind advice on terminology in the preparation of the English text of this edition.

Man and Animal

Pair-Formation in Ravens

KONRAD LORENZ

The dovetailing of certain instinctive behaviour patterns ensures
the coming together of two single animals to form a heterosexual
pair. From one group to another, even from one species to
another, these patterns can take very different forms. If we take
a panoramic view of the various types of pair-formation to be
found among the vertebrates, we find the following remarkable
state of affairs: some animal species as distant from one another
in the family tree as, for instance, birds and bony fish (Teleosti),
show very similar, even identical behaviour patterns. Furthermore, pair-formation in very many bird species may be reminis-
cent of that in a particular fish group; while other bird species
show behaviour which has close affinities to that of another family
of fish. The allocation of bird species to the two different groups
is by and large independent of their evolutionary relationships.
These parallels, therefore, can only be a result of convergence.
It is probable that such convergence came about because, for
those birds and fish which depend purely on eyesight, there are
only a limited number of possible ways in which the sexes can
find one another for the purpose of pair-formation. There can
hardly be any other reason to explain why we find again and
again the same type of sexual behaviour in forms of animal life
which in other respects differ so widely from each other. Among
the various 'methods' of pair-formation in birds there are two
distinct forms which, as already indicated, play a prominent part
in the class of birds.

With the first of these two different forms of pair-formation,
all the members of one sex show, under all circumstances,
instinctive behaviour patterns *different* from those of the members
of the other sex. Also, there is a no '*rank*' *relationship* between
the members of a pair. With the second type of pair-formation,

each individual fundamentally disposes of the whole range of instinctive behaviour patterns characteristic of both sexes: only through specific processes occurring in pair-formation is one or other 'set' of behaviour patterns suppressed so that each individual will then react in a purely feminine or purely masculine fashion. Furthermore, this kind of pair-formation *incorporates rank subordinance of the partner behaving in a female manner*. A. A. Allen refers to this as 'inferiorism'.

The first-mentioned kind of pair-formation, in which the partners confront each other as equals, is found, among the teleost fish, in some Chromids which can easily be observed in aquaria. Among the birds, herons belong to this group, as do cormorants and, most probably, many other species whose behaviour in this respect is still unknown. With all these animals *the sexes are of approximately equal size and their colouring is also approximately the same*. At least, there is never exclusive development by one sex of a 'display costume'. *The sole mechanism leading the partners of a pair together consists of sexually differentiated, instinctive behaviour patterns, which serve as sex-characteristics.* The male night-heron, for example, chooses, or acquires by fighting, a nesting site at the beginning of the breeding season. There is as yet no sign of his relating to a specific female. He defends this place against other males and, as his awakening instinctive patterns for nest-building are already becoming active, he utters a peculiar muted enticement call to draw the attention of all the unattached females to himself and his nest-building activities. When, finally, a female bird accepts the invitation of such a nest-offering male, courtship behaviour emerges in which both birds appear to behave in a roughly similar fashion. This does not, in contrast to the other group of birds to be described later, lead to the intimidation and subjugation of the female.[1]

In contrast to the animals in this first classification, which respond differently from the outset according to their sex, in the second group of species each individual possesses two sets of

[1] The differentiation of rank within a pair of night-herons, as described by Noble in 1938, is based on a misinterpretation of phenomena observed under conditions of captivity, when too many birds were kept in tiny aviaries.

instinctive sexual behaviour patterns, a masculine one and a feminine one – exhibiting so-called ambivalence. Only the process of pair-formation itself decides whether a certain individual will henceforth behave actively as a male or as a female. We find this type of pair-formation with some labyrinth fish and with most birds. Within both classes of animals there are some species in which both sexes look alike, along with those in which the male sex exhibits a distinctive display plumage. This kind of pair-formation takes a particularly interesting course *with those species where the members of both sexes look alike*. The question of exactly what induces the pairing of two individuals of opposite sexes in such species is not at all easy to answer since in captivity two members of the same sex, two males or two females, can very easily form a pair. I had a chance to investigate fairly intensively how homosexual pair-formation is prevented under natural conditions with my jackdaws and ravens. Since I was able to obtain some good slides[1] of the mating behaviour of ravens, I should like to describe in some detail the pair-formation of the raven as a typical example of a bird where both sexes look alike and the two sexes respond to each other with sexual ambivalence. Let me, however, preface this description with some theoretical remarks about the labyrinth fish type of pair-formation.

Unexpected as it sounds,[2] with the great majority of birds *it is*

[1] On which Hermann Kacher based the line drawings here reproduced. – Ed.

[2] On the other hand ambivalence of sexual behaviour fits in well with the rest of our knowledge of sex determination and sex differentiation. The fact that there is 'phenotypic' as well as 'genotypic' sex determination, in other words that here external environmental and there internal hereditary factors (e.g. the combination of x-chromosome and autosome substances in *Drosophila* fruit-flies) decide sex expression, can be considered only as a special instance of the general law of formation of characters. The switch can be operated externally as well as internally (viz. phenocopies). But, at least in many species, the autosomes probably provide the whole spectrum of variations of all characteristics from full masculinity to full femininity in every individual animal. This can be deduced not only from the well-known sex changes following castration or implantation of genital glands, and to a lesser degree after the injection of sex hormones, but also from the appearance of intersexual individuals which link both extremes on a continuous scale.

Even when the father bequeaths to his daughters female sex characteristics *the actual choice of a sexual partner which decides whether an individual will act like a male or a female.* This selection, this 'falling in love', which we describe as such for far better reasons than mere analogy, decides which of two alternative sets of instinctive behaviour patterns will be set in motion. With species in which this is so we can discriminate sharply between the masculine and the feminine sets of instinctive actions, because the two appear never to intermingle or to produce intermediary forms. The animal always responds to a specific partner in a

which he himself does not possess at all, as the bull, for instance, bequeaths the fat content of milk to his daughters, or the hind bequeaths the form of antlers to her sons, one can only explain this as suggested above. Finally, the development (e.g. in mammals) of the urogenital system together with the external sex organs, which are so extraordinarily different in males and females, begins with the same undifferentiated basic arrangement. The moment of decision as to whether the direction of future development will be male or female can vary enormously according to species and even race. There are species of frogs whose sex is already fixed in the first year of their lives. Others still vacillate in their fourth year.

While in the case of sex metamorphoses induced by secretion in vertebrates, physical characteristics in most cases go hand-in-hand with behaviour characteristics, these two factors seem to be sharply separated in the case of normal representatives of the bird and fish species which pair according to the labyrinth fish type.

Just as Spemann bridged the apparently fundamental contrast between mosaic and regulation eggs with the concept of determinism, and taught us to differentiate between types with early and late incidence of determination, one could say here: with those birds which pair in the manner of Chromids, physical characteristics and behavioural characteristics are determined early and roughly simultaneously. With those which behave in the manner of labyrinth fish, the determination of sexual behaviour is, on the contrary, postponed until the period of sexual maturity, thus being taken outside the realm of physiological development and into that of sexual experience of the mature individual. The concept of determinism is then, strictly speaking, no longer applicable, since this describes a process which takes place only once. One should say, rather, that behaviour may not be determined at all. The inherited alternative possibility of modification by choice will be decided either way through the psychological external factor, the phenomenon of 'falling in love'. This can happen, as often as the individual does in fact 'fall in love'. To 'fall in love' with a 'higher-ranking' partner liberates a fully female range of behaviour; to 'fall in love' with a 'lower-ranking' partner will liberate full male sexual behaviour. Intersexual behaviour does not occur, but the alternatives can be changed every time a new pair-formation takes place. – Otto Koehler.

purely masculine or a purely feminine fashion. Even when, because of the change of partner, sexual behaviour may change suddenly into its opposite, there is never an intermediate form of behaviour.

W. Craig was the first to prove this state of affairs experimentally with pigeons. With all the species of pigeons which had previously been investigated, every bird kept isolated for some time had shown behaviour generally known as the 'male' courting display. But when Craig introduced to such an isolated bird, which had been conducting itself as a male, another bird of the same species, but one which showed a stronger and more passionate nature, the courting display of the first bird quickly disappeared, to be replaced by behaviour which could only be described as that of a *female* invitation to courtship. It was quite immaterial for this whole process what the sex of either bird was, neither was it necessary for the birds to have actual physical contact. All that was necessary to extinguish the courting display of the weaker bird was to put the cages close to one another.

There can be no doubt that this inability to continue to act like a male in face of a stronger partner of the same species is based on a kind of intimidation. In the natural state, too, it may often be observed how a weaker male will yield to a stronger one, preferring flight to combat. Under natural conditions, however, where free choice of sex partners is present, wild birds probably do not exhibit any sexual bonding between two males, which would lead to exhibition of the female set of instinctive behaviour patterns by the weaker partner. Heinroth very aptly defined such instinctive behaviour patterns, which combine the function of threat against other males with that of courtship of the female, as *Imponiergehaben* ('demonstrative behaviour'). Any weaker male reacts to the demonstrative behaviour of the stronger male by flight: there is no need for preliminary fighting. This particular form of intimidation seems to me to be the primary condition, in all birds with ambivalent responses, for the individual to be able to respond as a female. Isolated birds of both sexes always respond in a masculine fashion; as I have demonstrated with my jackdaws, even strong females in a group will do this, as long as they are at the apex of the social order.

Grasl, the Viennese importer of animals and breeder of parrots, observed a peculiar form of the same behaviour in *Poephila acuticauda* (the long-tailed finch). In this species, both sexes look alike. If he put a bird previously kept separate in with another of the same species, they would almost always immediately proceed to mate. He intended to use this response for discovering the sex of the birds, but soon found out that this was impossible. When he put one bird into a cage with another, they would mate with each other at once, but always in the following manner: the bird which was already in the cage took over the part of the male and the newcomer that of the female. Because of the recent change of surroundings, the newly arrived bird would be much too intimidated to be motivated for self-assertion, which is necessary for the performance of demonstrative display. Because of this, it would at once respond to the imposing conspecific with instinctive 'female' behaviour, quite irrespective of whether it was a male or a female.

If all wild individuals of a species responded in this ambiguous way, at least half of all pairs formed would be homosexual. The question is how this is prevented. With many species, for instance with grebes, some rails, pigeons, and others, we know virtually nothing about this. With very many birds which show identical colouring in both sexes, the body-size along with general vigour and the urge for activity of the male exceed those of the female, and this plays an important part in the formation of appropriate pairs. According to A. A. Allen, only size and aggression serve as sex differentiation signals in *Bonasa umbellus* (the ruffed grouse, an American forest fowl). He introduced a particularly strong and vigorous female to the weakest of all the males in his possession, which had taken beatings from all its companions, with the result that pairing took place – but with reversed roles. The sex glands of such an intimidated male exhibiting female behaviour do not show the increase in size which normally takes place in the breeding season.

The relationship between behaviour and the maturation process of the sex organs varies enormously among the ambivalent species of birds. With some pairs of females, the partner which behaves like a male lays eggs, for instance in the case of pigeons

and the Chiloë wigeon (*Mareca sibilatrix*). With Canada geese
the dominant female does not lay eggs; this seems to be equally
the case with domestic hens which behave like males. Blocking of
the maturation process of the testes in the 'inferioristic' *Bonasa*
males, as observed by Allen, need not by any means be directly
connected with behaviour; the perpetual persecution by superior
males can physically damage the victim to such a degree that the
breeding characteristics fail to appear. Only the failure of higher-
ranking females to lay eggs, therefore, can be taken as the direct
consequence of the external stimulus situation.

We have seen that with many species the difference in body
size makes it improbable that a female will assume the role of
the intimidating partner with male behaviour. There is also a
large group of species which possess the specific morphological
characters of the male 'display costume'. In some cases, this has
an exclusive effect on the females and attracts them, as Darwin
observed. These species include, on the one hand, the ruffs,
blackcocks, peacocks, probably many birds of paradise and others;
in these species, the males do not fight each other seriously
– they have instead a so-called social courtship display, which
they perform communally at specific sites. With most of these
splendidly attired birds, on the other hand, the conspicuous
costume not only attracts a female which is 'selecting' a mate,
but also has an at least equivalent effect of intimidating *all* other
members of the species. This also occurs with reptiles and many
fish. Lissman observed that the females of the fighting fish (*Betta
splendens*) did not dare to fight the males, which were much
smaller and weaker than them, because they were intimidated
by the males spreading out their fins in demonstrative display.
In birds, a splendidly developed male display costume is in most
cases a demonstrative symbol which works on the female by first
intimidating her and thus inhibiting her male 'set of drives';
only as a secondary effect does it release her specifically female
responses. Furthermore, with such species, which exhibit strong
sexual dimorphism, any female is destined to be inferior in rank
to any male. These same females do, however, show the latent,
ever-present ambivalence of their instinctive equipment if they
are kept without males. They then perform the entire range of

male behaviour patterns. As every breeder knows, when there is no cock in the farmyard, the hen highest in rank will invariably begin to behave as if she were a cock. So even domestic fowl, in spite of their great difference in plumage, basically show the same duality of instinctive equipment as the pigeons, jackdaws, and others already described.

The effectiveness of the male's display costume is essentially manifested in the fact that it is much more difficult for a pair of two such males to be formed than with the birds mentioned earlier, the male and the female of which look alike. While with pigeons, jackdaws, geese, swans, and other species, in which the sexes resemble each other, pairs consisting of males are as frequently and easily formed as pairs consisting of females, and can just as easily be put together experimentally – we find that with pheasants, domestic fowl, or sexually dimorphic ducks, two males practically never form a pair. This is apparently because the permanently displayed plumage prevents other males from assuming a male to be a female. This display costume operates, as it were, as a 'frozen demonstrative gesture' and is doubtless so imbedded in the identity of the individual male that he would find performance of female behaviour difficult. With these species, the modest-looking female can, to be sure, develop the full demonstrative behaviour of the male, and exhibit it to other females; but the far more highly differentiated male cannot reverse the differentiation of his courtship display and assume the role of the female. To my knowledge there has been only a single case in which a male of a species with strong sexual dimorphism could be observed to show the whole gamut of 'female' behaviour, in contrast to innumerable known examples of female pair-formation within the same species. This single exception was one of a pair of *Lampronessa sponsa* (Carolina wood duck) formed by two males kept by Heinroth.

If, after all this, the display costume of the males of birds with sexual dimorphism in coloration plays no more fundamental a role than does the difference in size and the somewhat greater activity of the males in other species, then it cannot reliably prevent homosexual pair-formation, which is deleterious to perpetuation of the species. As mentioned above, it is the choice of the partner which decides whether one or the other of the two latently existing sets of instinctive responses will manifest itself in a bird. With those birds which are sexually ambivalent, the choice of a partner seems to be the only process which, directly and apparently by hormonal means, is decided by the existence of one or other of the sex glands. It is experimentally possible to induce a male turtle-dove, jackdaw, or mute swan to 'fall in love' with another male. But if we observe, in a larger flock, the free choice of sexual partners, as I was able to do accurately with tame, free-flying jackdaws, we find out quite soon that, beyond doubt, the males will 'fall in love' only with lower-ranking females and the females will 'fall in love' only with higher-ranking males. With herring-gulls (*Larus argentatus*) the same apparently happens, although the body-weight of the sexes overlaps considerably and the males are only on average, and by no means invariably, heavier than the females. When Goethe measured them he did not find a single pair where the male was lighter in weight than the female! This hormonally conditioned choice of a stronger or weaker sexual partner does in practice guarantee production of heterosexual pairs, provided that the bird at the apex of the rank order is a male and that a female occupies the lowest rung.

This should nearly always be the case with sexually determined size-differences in the natural state. Many homosexual unions produced under experimental conditions are dissolved when a fully developed partner of the same species, but of the other sex, is introduced; with others the personal bond survives, as with domestic pigeons and particularly with some geese. The introduction of an appropriate sex partner often has a truly surprising effect. Craig justifiably calls it one of the most impressive sights in nature to see a turtle-dove, which is in every respect an impassioned, belligerent male, turn into a 'gentle virgin' within a few minutes when a real male, a stronger bird, is put in with it. I observed an even more sudden transformation with a ruddy shelduck (*Casarca ferruginea*). My friend Antonius from the Vienna (Schönbrunn) Zoo loaned me a pair, the male of which was a New Zealand black Casarca (*Casarca variegata*) while the female belonged to the rust-coloured Eastern European variety. I had known both birds for years and, like Professor Antonius, had no doubts about their sex. However, as soon as I let them out on my pond, the ruddy shelduck immediately demonstrated a strong attraction to an unmated female Egyptian goose (*Alopochen aegyptiaca*) and after only a few hours was producing the full male courting song of the red Casarca, which we had never heard in all the years of its stay at Schönbrunn! The bird really was a male, as I was able to observe beyond doubt on the occasion of subsequent matings, through the presence of a penis, and by the later production of hybrids. It is reasonable to assume that this red Casarca had been forced into the female role because all its companions of the same genus were stronger and therefore higher-ranking. All the other Casarcas in the zoo had been of the New Zealand variety, which is much stronger and is also more belligerent than the Eastern European variety. This particularly ruddy shelduck assumed a hostile attitude towards its former homosexual partner from the moment of its conversion from female to male behaviour.

A female raven behaved differently in a similar situation. In the spring of 1932 I had two one-year-old ravens which conducted a courtship display quite like old-timers in spite of their immaturity, so that I then took them for a pair because of their mutual courtship. I had to keep these two birds locked up to protect them from savage persecution by my free-flying pair of tame ravens, which were a year older. Later on there were disturbances in the love-life of the older pair, which will be discussed later, and these quarrels finally ended when the older female flew away, never to return. When I let the two one-year-old ravens, which had formed a pair, out into the field with the other male, I found to my astonishment that the bird which up till now had behaved like a male at once responded in a female fashion to the courtship display of the older male and soon afterwards mated with him. This female did not, however, immediately give up her love relationship with the one-year-old female, but for some time continued to play the role of the male with her. Estrangement between them set in only gradually. Although intermediate behaviour patterns or transitional stages never occur, so that male and female behaviour patterns are always sharply distinguished, both forms of behaviour may still be exhibited one after the other, and even alternating behaviour of the same individual with two different partners is known to occur. The old female jackdaw already mentioned, which had been forced into the role of the male because she was the highest-ranking bird of the colony, later behaved like the year-old female raven. When a very strong old male returned to the colony after an absence of two years, the old female at once 'fell in love' with him and mated with him, but without giving up her relationship with the younger female of inferior rank which had been her partner before.

All species of birds in which each individual disposes of the instinctive behaviour patterns of both sexes form pairs only after a rank relationship has been established in which the male ranks above the female. But there are quite a number of species of birds which respond in this ambivalent fashion, where the order of rank between mates never becomes apparent, simply because the individuals never fall out with one another, never fight and always appear to be hand-in-glove. With these species especially, the instinctive ceremony of pair-formation very clearly reflects the original fight for supremacy which has the function of re-pressing the female's male responses through intimidation. Real fights never take place and the male's intimidating demonstrative behaviour quite suffices. We find a typical example of such ceremonially modified rank-fighting in the 'amorous play' of numerous fish, particularly labyrinth fish, and in a markedly altered, specialised form in the Cichlid *Hemichromis* and others. As far as we know, labyrinth fish and many Cichlids are, apart from birds, the only creatures where every individual possesses the full range of instinctive responses of both sexes. A different example is provided by the pair-formation of the raven, which we shall deal with next. The above preamble was necessary in order that the following facts may be properly understood.

The maturing raven exhibits sexual responses long before it is capable of reproduction; it assumes courting postures, tries to mate with other ravens, and so on. In particular, birds which are only a few months old display the female mating invitation – squatting down flat and rapidly fluttering the partly spread wings and tail feathers. Tame birds use this behaviour pattern as an expression of 'general devotion' to their keepers, so that, years ago, when I had no experience of the duplicity of the sexual behaviour of these birds, I always thought that all my young ravens were females. From what has been said above, and remembering that the tame animal considers its keeper in his position of power as superior in rank, the female behaviour of young birds can be easily understood. No tame male raven has ever dared to confront me with the masculine demonstrative display. But if a male raven meets for the first time another of its own kind which excites it sexually, then it assumes the demonstrative display posture shown in Figs. 1 and 2 and walks towards the stranger in this posture. The stranger, in turn, assumes the same posture and moves forward towards the other raven with peculiar, strutting steps, which give even the human observer the impression of deliberate tension and display. The two then circle around or walk alongside each other for some time, attempting to 'impress' one another. Then a peculiar, low-pitched, painful-sounding, choking call is emitted, which Heinroth spells 'au' or 'rau'. I find it spelled in my diary as 'chrrua'. The sound costs the bird considerable effort; it bends forward while producing it, spreads its tail feathers and holds its wing elbows away from its body. This posture is otherwise only assumed when the bird is calling at the top of its voice. The head feathers are ruffled to their limit. During this 'bowing' ceremony the birds move nearer to each other and jostle each other lightly while stepping about side by side. During this performance, which is functionally clearly allied to demonstrative behaviour and corresponds to the 'charging' of male pigeons, it is by no means clear which bird will take on the part of the male and which will play the female. It is equally possible that both birds will behave in a male fashion and begin to fight a moment later. In this case there emerge the body-posture and feather arrangement seen in Fig. 4. In a demonstrative display similar to that shown in Figs. 1 and 2, the bird's head feathers are abruptly flattened, but in this case the feathers remain extremely ruffled in a narrow, sharply circumscribed area around each eye, so that, most surprisingly, there appear to be two feathered horns or ears, a phenomenon which was observed by Heinroth. This display is equivalent to a declaration of war; a moment later, the bird with the 'ears' will seize the other with its claws with the ferocity of a bird of prey at the kill.

Figs. 1 and 2. Male raven in demonstrative display posture.

If the 'bowing ceremony' is not to become a fight, one of the two birds must now yield, that is allow itself to be pushed farther and farther back. Both will then stride alongside each other over a large area, constantly bowing and uttering 'chrrua' calls, with one of them continuing to advance and the other persistently

29

Fig. 3.   *Bowing ceremony of ravens.*

Fig. 4.   *Male raven in threat posture
with 'horns'.*

retreating. It is this retreating which excludes performance of the ceremony on trees and seems to be the reason why it nearly always takes place on the ground.

When this activity has been going on for a very long time – with young birds it continues for days – the more aggressive bird

Figs. 5 and 6.   'Choking' movements of male raven.

will gradually switch to another behaviour pattern. Instead of producing the 'chrrua' call, after a peculiar choking movement the bird emits a comparatively subdued and high-pitched nasal call, which may be roughly rendered as 'chrujuju'. At the same time it lifts its strongly ruffled head, which is now thrust very far forward, a little above the horizontal level. Simultaneously it spreads its wings, stretches them backwards, and pulls the nictitating membrane over the eye, which suddenly looks white (Figs. 5, 6, and 7), especially if its excitement increases. It seems strange that the bird should render itself blind in this manner at the very moment when it is preparing to be so active. During this ceremony the female or, more precisely, the bird behaving

31

in a female manner, all the time yields to the partner's advance. Fig. 7 very clearly shows the female bird in retreat.

This choking movement, and all the other ceremonies of the male raven described here, are good examples of what I call 'releasers', namely instinctive behaviour patterns which have the sole biological purpose of releasing a corresponding instinctive pattern in a partner of the same species. The choking ceremony, in particular, is a beautiful demonstration of how a bird which has no especially stimulating physical characteristics such as

Fig. 7. Climax of male raven's 'choking' movement.

colourful feathers or distendable and conspicuously coloured naked parts of the body, can produce peculiar visual stimuli by using available characteristics and simply taking up an unusual posture. Perhaps only the elongated neck feathers of the raven, shaped like lancets, may be regarded as morphological releasers; their splendid highlights are strikingly shown in Fig. 8. In response to all this, the 'female' raven arrests her bowing ceremony, but only very gradually. By degrees, she takes up a flattened, crouching posture and eventually assumes, with quivering wings and tail, the familiar female mating posture of the domestic hen. At this moment she utters a low, hoarse call. Hooded crows utter approximately the same characteristic call, as I have observed with tame birds which performed this instinctive behaviour pattern towards their keeper. It by no means necessarily follows that true mating will take place; on the contrary, the double ceremony frequently breaks down at this point. By squatting down the female symbolises her submission, and finally by giving up her perpetual retreat she permits the male to approach her. She then falls into a state of ecstatic quivering with her tail, while the male, no less ecstatic, utters nasal sounds and stretches his neck forward. With startling suddenness, both birds appear to have completely calmed down and fly away, usually together.

Fig. 8. Male and female raven immediately before mating.

To be quite accurate, I must mention that the 'docility ceremony' which I have just described never ran its full course with my first pair of ravens, which were the models for most of the illustrations here reproduced. In Fig. 8 the female stands atypically far away from the male while executing the instinctive behaviour pattern of crouching and quivering with her tail. This was because, just at the time when the docility ceremony should have taken place, there occurred instead a blocking of the normal development of pair-formation. She did not wait for the approach of the vigorously courting male, but always evaded him at the last moment and jumped away sideways. The male would try again and again to come near to the female with his head pushed forward and his nictitating membrane over his eyes. He even assumed this docility posture in flight, when pursuing the female through the air (Fig. 9). As the female evaded his approaches over and over again, he began instead to show the feathered 'ears' described above, and his docility changed into fury. Finally the pursuits degenerated to such an extent that the female flew away estranged, never to return. To our surprise, the male who had stayed behind then mated with the other immature female mentioned earlier, in a normal progression of pair-forming ceremonies. I explain the failure of pair-formation with the

Fig. 9.   Pair of ravens in flight, with male 'choking'.

first two-year-old female by the previous history of the birds. The two had grown up together and spent many months locked up in one small aviary. During this time the female had grown so used to retreating before the stronger male that later she could not hold firm against his approach. Perhaps it is absolutely necessary that the partners should not have known each other beforehand, or at least should not be fixated in a definite status relationship with each other.

In the later phases of pair-bonding between the male and the younger female, the entire system of species-specific instinctive behaviour patterns described above gradually disappeared, as the two birds became more intimate. In the end there was nothing more to be seen of the retreat of the female or the pursuit by the male. It would hardly have been possible, moreover, to confirm a relationship based on status between these two birds, since their mutual compatibility had never suffered any disturbance. The demonstrative behaviour which is a basic requirement in the instinctive courtship display of the male for the purpose of blocking any possible masculine behaviour by the female is therefore, in ravens, limited to the period of pair-formation. Pigeons, by

Fig. 10. *Male raven caressing neck of female.*

contrast, continue to perform a series of instinctive patterns which demonstrate the superior position of the male with respect to the female, even when the pair have been mated for some considerable time. This is shown, for instance, by the way in which the female pigeon will be driven back to the nest by methods which can only be described as rough. The total absence of fear towards her mate in the female raven is shown in Fig. 10, which shows the female allowing the male to caress her neck.

Most unfortunately, I did not have the chance to continue my observations on the reproductive biology of this particular pair because one day the male failed to come home, undoubtedly shot by an unknown miscreant.

On the Psychology of the Horse

BERNHARD GRZIMEK

Among the domestic animals which man has adopted not only
for their physical qualities but also for their intelligence, the horse
comes second only to the dog. Although man has lived with
horses for thousands of years, he has made little study of their
psychology. The famous books of the great riding masters of the
eighteenth century give information only on how to 'break in'
the horse and how to advance its physical development. The
military instructions on horsemanship of the last century were
similarly conceived; the horse was then still of vital importance
to the striking force of the army. But in the year 1904 a horse
named Kluger Hans ('Clever Hans'), belonging to Herr von
Osten, attracted much attention in Germany and throughout the
world. Although scientific tests proved that this horse could not
read or count, and that it could not answer questions, it did
respond with incredible sensitivity, through communication by
knocks, to the unconscious signals of its master and trainer. The
same was claimed of the stallions of Karl Krall of Elberfeld,
which were supposed to be capable of reading Gothic, Latin, and
Greek letters, of understanding German and French, and solving
cubic roots. The book which Krall published in 1912 about these
'thinking horses' directed attention to their psychology, and
probably stimulated Maday to write his more scientific work *The
Psychology of the Horse and Dressage*, and Dr Emil Hauck his
Psychological Behaviour of Horses and Dogs (1928). But even these
books merely noted anecdotes from literature and personal
observation, without the benefit of the critical experimental
methods since developed by modern ethologists for their research. They quoted examples of dogs and horses which were
believed to express philosophical attitudes through the language

of bells and knocks, and were influenced by human psychology, which was itself influenced by philosophy.

Since I have ridden horses since my youth, and have had a lot to do with them professionally, I have tried to learn, through experiment, something about the psychology of the horse.

To gain some idea of how an animal sees the world, and therefore of the kind of 'environment' in which it lives, it is necessary to examine the capacities of its sense organs. Up to the most recent literature one repeatedly finds the assertion that the higher animals are totally colour-blind. This is quite true of some nocturnal animals, for instance bats and lemurs. Quite a number of species of insects and fish have been examined for their ability to discriminate between colours, but only a few of the higher mammals have been investigated in a reliable manner. The colour sense of the apes is excellent, the chimpanzee being even a little superior to man, whereas mice, rats, hedgehogs, squirrels, rabbits, racoons, cats, and dogs are only partly colour-sensitive with wide individual differences.

I trained two horses over the course of several weeks to take oats from one particular box out of a series of six to ten. All the boxes were of the same shape, but for training purposes one bore a specially coloured plate, yellow for instance. All boxes contained oats, so that the horses were not able to orientate themselves by smell. All the boxes but the one with the coloured plate carried plates of a number of graded tones of grey – in all twenty-seven grades from white to black. To a totally colour-blind creature, the yellow would appear as a grey tone, as in a black and white photograph, and the coloured plate would therefore be indistinguishable from one of the many different light and dark grey ones. My horses did not do this; after some weeks' training with different colours they chose the yellow, the green, the blue, or the red correctly in 54 to 98·6 per cent of cases. The training with red was the most difficult for the two horses, taking the longest time and producing the fewest correct results; even so, the horses correctly chose the red box from five grey ones in as many as 54·5 to 70·4 per cent of cases. The training was much easier with blue, and the percentage of correct choices much higher; results were better still with green, and by far the best were obtained with yellow. With this colour one of the horses achieved 94·4 per cent correct choice, and the other 98·6 per cent. To exclude the possibility that the training colour might appear as a particular grey tone, I used, for example in the green colour training, not the customary green plate but sometimes a light green or a dark green one, which to the colour-blind would appear as a quite different shade of grey. The horses were not confused by this. Colour discrimination by cattle, zebras, giraffes, and meerkats was demonstrated to me in a similar manner by colleagues at the Frankfurt Zoological Gardens.

Later I steadily decreased the size of the coloured plates in the experiments with my horses, so that finally there remained only narrow vertical stripes of varying widths. The horse used for these experiments had to decide, at a distance of several yards, between two branches of a path, whether it was going towards a coloured or a grey stripe. In this manner I was also able to gain evidence of the horses' visual acuity.

Even among experienced horsemen there is a widespread belief that horses see everything much enlarged, and that they shy because of this. Such an idea is absurd, since the size of the inverse image on the retina, which changes in accordance with the design of the eye in animals of different species, is irrelevant. From the image on the retina, the brain quite accurately 'calculates' the correct size of the replicated, real object. Any animal species in which this did not apply would have disappeared from the earth long ago. All the same, I was able to verify that the eyesight of horses is inferior to that of human beings; and that with horses, as with man, the accuracy of vision in respect of the colour blue is considerably less than, for instance, that in respect of yellow.

When Alexander the Great allowed himself to be represented on horseback by the famous painter Apelles in Ephesus, the king was not satisfied with the way his favourite horse Bucephalos had been painted. He arranged for the horse to be taken before the picture in order to reproach the artist with some of the faults of the painting. As soon as Bucephalos saw his picture he neighed, and Apelles thereupon said with a smile: 'O King, your horse seems to understand more about painting than you do.' To my satisfaction, a couple of millennia later I have been able to prove that the neighing of Bucephalos was in fact no proof of the quality of his portrait.

My object was to discover whether horses recognise sculptured or two-dimensional images of themselves at all. As always with researches into behaviour, it is only possible to draw conclusions about such psychological processes in animals empirically through their behaviour, since we are not in a position to ask them questions. I first collected thirty-six horses which were strangers to one another and paired them off. It turned out that two strange horses would approach each other with their heads held high and their ears pointing forward. They would smell each other's nostrils first, then the tails and certain other parts of the body. In addition, they would always stick together in an alien environment.

Having determined the behaviour of one horse towards other living horses, I confronted over a hundred horses with a life-size stuffed horse, and then with various life-size pictures of horses. The stuffed horse was greeted in exactly the same way as a living one, and treated as such. The horses placed themselves next to the dummy, side by side with it. Whenever I chased one of them away from the manger with my whip, it would vent its fury on the defenceless dummy, galloping towards it, biting it, kicking it, and even knocking it over. Human beings vent their spite in a similar manner on their subordinates when they have been scolded by superiors. Even a rudimentary, life-size horse-image made from wrapping paper had its nose and tail sniffed; the horses were not to be lured away from it and stallions even tried to mate with it. Even completely schematised horse dummies with straight legs like pillars and angular outlines were treated, up to a point, like members of the same species. But only a few horses were interested in dummy dogs, and then only those who had been in a friendly relationship with a particular dog. Apelles would have been abashed to see what simplified and distorted images, worthy of a modern artist, are acceptable to horses, treated as horses, and fully acknowledged as such.

Later I offered an artificial zebra to wild zebras in the Ngorongoro Crater in Tanzania. They, too, were interested in it, and approached it quite closely, putting their noses to that of the dummy and to its tail.

Shying is a particularly fear-inspiring characteristic of horses. Even today more people are killed and wounded by shying horses than by lions and tigers and all the large predators put together. It was not easy to investigate shying with my experimental animals, since they were all familiar with traffic in the streets of Berlin and not at all easily disturbed. I investigated in particular one kind of shying which can bring a rider to despair: the obstinate refusal to pass certain objects which are unusual or which are new in a familiar environment. It is often necessary to apply every trick known to a horseman to make a horse pass a sheet of newspaper lying in a ditch. Few of the three hundred animals which I used in experiments feared anything at all. Neither a frightening buzzing noise, nor a basin full of horse's blood, nor highly coloured cardboard discs on the ground made any impression. Finally I built a doorway and put behind it the life-size cardboard dummy of a dog whose head wobbled, and installed bundles of twigs in the doorway in front of it so that the approaching horse had to force its way through. Contrary to expectations, the younger horses shied less than the older ones, and the thoroughbreds less than the others who were otherwise more placid.

Attempts at camouflage by changes of dress have shown that horses recognise people with whom they are familiar by their total appearance. The face does not initially play an important role, any more than any other similarly sized surface of the body. Horses are very easily deceived by clothing, and probably learn only very gradually, through familiarity with people whom they see every day and who frequently wear different clothing, that the face is the only part of the human figure which always remains the same.

Many animals have what seems a miraculous ability to find their way; for instance birds that migrate south, and then leave Africa to find their way back to their nesting places on the Baltic Sea. In the last few years it has been discovered that bees use polarised light from the sky as a compass, and ants and starlings use the position of the sun. Many horsemen observed during the First World War that horses could take them safely back to their unit and stable when human beings had completely lost their bearings. The rider had only to put the reins on the neck of the horse and leave it all to the animal. This resulted in the belief that horses have a kind of sixth sense, a 'homing instinct'.

The truth would seem to be that horses, the modern descendants of the original roamers of the steppe, merely have an excellent memory for landscape and for paths which have been trodden before. To eliminate any possibility that my horses relied on anything other than their memory of streets they had used before and their sense of locality, I used thoroughbred Arab mares which had never been ridden or harnessed and which had been used for breeding at the great Janow-Podlaski stud in Poland. They knew only their stables and the enclosure in front of them. I blindfolded these horses and transported them in a lorry various distances from their home stud. Then I took off their blindfolds and let them run free. Not one of them found its way home. Instead, they made for any hamlet in the vicinity, remaining near houses and human habitations. They always avoided passing through forests. The behaviour of these animals gives no grounds for believing that horses have an inherent sense of direction towards their home ground. I am, however, convinced that horses which had previously travelled these streets either saddled or in the shafts of a carriage would have found their way home without much difficulty.

I investigated the memory horses have for certain processes – in particular for the disappearance of food – by pouring oats into one of four covered boxes in front of a horse's eyes. The horse was then allowed to walk from its stand to the boxes and to eat the oats from the box which had just been filled. Even to an experienced horseman it will be incomprehensible that a horse cannot immediately grasp what seems an obvious connection. My horses went as often to the other boxes as to the one into which the food had just been put. It took very lengthy and tedious training to induce the animals to open first the box which had just been filled in front of their eyes. When that lesson had sunk in, the horses were no longer allowed to approach and feed immediately from the boxes which had just been filled, but had to wait for varying periods of time. One horse could keep the newly filled box in mind for only six seconds; the second horse could remember it for sixty. After a longer interval it would again try all the other boxes.

By contrast, experiments with dogs and ravens have shown that they remember for hours food which has been buried in their sight, and my wolves retained such a memory for days. It should not be concluded from such experiments that a horse has a much poorer memory in general; *only that it has a very short memory for these particular processes.* The hiding of food plays no part in the life of grazing animals, while prey often hides from the wolf, which is a hunter. It is probable that in respect of territorial recognition and dominance fighting, for example, the memory of grazers is incomparably better.

Before attempting to judge the intelligence of an animal it is necessary to know, in the first place, which are innate instinctive behaviour patterns and which are acquired by experience in the life of the individual. This has been determined beyond doubt only with small animals, notably birds. With some birds, the species-specific song is innate. A blackbird which has been artificially hatched and brought up in isolation sings the right song as soon as it is sexually mature; nor does the ring-dove, the domestic cock or the nightjar need to hear and learn the calls typical of its species. On the other hand, chaffinches or nightingales which have been brought up in isolation cannot sing like their fellows until they have heard the species-typical song.

Specific equine behaviour shown by a horse which has been brought up in isolation must therefore be innate instinctive behaviour. To establish this, I attended the birth of a horse, took the newborn foal as soon as it left the mother's body and wrapped it in blankets. I brought it up artificially, entirely isolated from other horses. I was able to list a whole series of instinctive behaviour patterns which this animal had brought with it from its mother's body, since it could not have observed them in another horse.

In human beings, left- and right-handedness is a psychological attribute which is inherited. I was able to establish that among the larger parrots 45·8 per cent of birds are 'right-handed', that is, they stand on their left foot while eating, and regularly use their right foot to take food to their beaks. In monkeys there is no sign that one paw is preferred to the other. Horses often chew very asymmetrically, grinding with their lower jaws in one direction only. With the help of an apparatus strapped to the horse to register its chewing movements, I confirmed that of ten horses, eight were 'right-chewers', that is they moved their lower jaws only to the right and not in both directions.

I observed fifty-three horses, in experiments lasting for several weeks: (1) pawing in front of a bowl of food which they could not reach, (2) stepping over an obstacle at a walk, (3) taking their first step when walking, and (4) galloping without a rider. When pawing, 77 per cent of horses were one-handed, preferring one foreleg; 58·5 per cent preferred the right leg, 41·4 per cent the left. When stepping over an obstacle, not even one in ten horses was one-handed, i.e. chose to use one particular leg first. I let these same horses stand quietly and then brought them out of their boxes to watch them move. Two-thirds started to walk with one particular foreleg; of these 55 per cent were right-handed and 45 per cent left-handed. When galloping without a rider, only 23 per cent favoured one particular form of gallop. When galloping 30 per cent stepped off with the right foreleg and the other 70 per cent with the left. This contradicts the common horseman's claim that all untrained horses step off with the left leg first in galloping. We human beings are 100 per cent one-handed, and 95 per cent are right-handed. No human being uses both hands or eyes to the same degree. A much smaller proportion of horses are one-handed, and among these right-handed and left-handed are about equally represented. The one-handedness of horses does not originate with their training as riding or carriage horses, as I was able to prove with young untrained horses.

Human beings innately and instinctively form a *social system* or hierarchy when living together in large numbers for any length of time. Schjelderup-Ebbe proved fifty years ago that domestic fowl have a similar tendency to form hierarchies. The birds do not peck each other at random. For each chicken it is laid down which birds it may drive away from food and from which it must accept pecks without retaliating. In the community to which it belongs each chicken therefore has 'superiors' and 'inferiors'.

I investigated several herds of horses to find out whether a similar hierarchy was present with them. This was less easy to establish than with domestic fowl, because horses are more peace-loving and do not bite each other as readily as fowl peck at each other. I painted a large number on both flanks of each horse so that I could distinguish them more easily and note every hostile act among them. First I let them go hungry for a day, then put a single bucket of oats in the middle of the stable yard to provoke quarrels. There was seldom any serious kicking and biting. Instead the dominant animal had only to indicate with a movement of its head its intention to bite, or by a typical posture of its body, by lifting a foot for instance, to show that it intended to kick. This gesture was immediately understood by the lower-ranking animal, which would then make room for the dominant animal. In this manner I was able to recognise a firm hierarchy within separate herds of mares and stallions. This hierarchy had hardly changed when I checked it two months later. Yet the highest-ranking stallion did not determine the herd's direction of movement when it was grazing, or when it was being pursued. This proved to be the function of the lower-ranking animals. With the herd of mares, the highest-ranking ones often isolated themselves at considerable distances from the other animals, and grazed by themselves.

I have been able to sketch some of the characteristics that may be included in our picture of the psychology of the horse. It goes without saying that far more detailed studies will be necessary before we have even an approximately accurate conception of the horse's psychology.

Animal Meals

KARL VON FRISCH

Human meals are complicated affairs. Much must be considered before a choice is finally made, seasoning is then added, the food is roasted, boiled, or baked, and garnishing completes the process. It is obvious that animals behave differently in this respect. It is less well known how varied the meals of animals and their preparations are, how different from human procedure, yet how sensible and imaginative.

Let us begin with the meals of the water-flea, an extreme contrast to what is most appetising to a human gourmet. For goodness sake, you will think, here we are rejoicing that fleas have almost entirely died out in our society, and suddenly you tell us there are fleas in our water! Don't worry. They are only given that name because when they swim they make movements similar to those of fleas. They might be said to execute a kind of hopping movement, as fleas do on dry land. In reality they are tiny crustaceans, like minute lobsters, smaller than a pin-head. Ecologically they have a very important role to play, in spite of their small size. Let us imagine that we are crossing a lake in a boat, towing behind us a net of very fine mesh. When we have covered, say, a hundred yards, we haul in the net and empty its contents into a bowl of water. The layman will be astonished by the teeming multitude of tiny creatures captured from the clear lake water, in which, from the boat, we couldn't see a single living creature, except perhaps a fish here and there. There is a very large number of water-fleas in our catch. They form an important ingredient in the nourishment of freshwater fish. But what is their own nourishment? If prizes were given for a particularly crude way of acquiring sustenance, then water-fleas would qualify beyond doubt for first prize. From early morning till evening and from evening till morning they do nothing but swim to and fro, with great regularity, in order to filter the water through which they propel themselves with the movements of their tiny legs. These legs are microscopic works of art. They are thickly planted with delicate criss-cross bristles, forming a kind of filtering apparatus which sieves out still smaller creatures floating about in the water, invisible to the human eye. They also have bristles which sweep and bristles which cram, collecting automatically with repetitive sweeping movements everything that accumulates on their filters and then cramming it into their mouths. In this way, constant, unselective filtering and feeding takes place, with the result that these pygmies flourish and proliferate in enormous quantities.

It is not only dwarfs in the animal world which gain their livelihood by such filtering techniques. The very largest among the giants of the animal world, the whales, use the same methods. The mouth of a whale-bone whale has an enormous cubic capacity. When the whale opens its mouth there stream into it, carried in a flood of sea-water, a multitude of sea creatures – molluscs, crustaceans, and others – the largest only an inch or so in length. When it closes its mouth and squeezes the water out again, it retains all the nourishing small fry with the sieve which it has in place of teeth. Thousands of such sea creatures are just about enough for one good gulp. Among the most dreaded pirates of the sea, the sharks, there is one particularly large species, the basking shark, which does not attack anybody, but lives in a similar manner to whales and water-fleas, by unselective filtering of comparatively small prey.

Whales and water-fleas are really exceptions in their feeding methods. Most animals deliberately choose their food. What they choose differs a good deal from animal to animal and frequently corresponds not at all with our own tastes. There is no accounting for tastes – the old saying is especially apt when applied to the animal world in all its variety. To a dung-beetle there is nothing more delicious than the smell of cow dung, and a cow pat, to which it is led by its sense of smell, is the ultimate of culinary delight. The famous *Scarabaeus*, which was sacred to the ancient Egyptians, makes a kind of cult of moulding the dung it finds into a neatly shaped ball, and then rolling it over the ground. The

47

male and female labour together over this task. Finally they take the ball into a hole in the ground where, before laying eggs on it, they first feast off it together.

Even if we can appreciate the food value of this meal – for in the faeces of all mammals there exist many alimentary products which may be extracted and used – many a housewife will wonder what makes her clothes-moths grow fat. No human being would think of chewing his pullover or his fur collar, even during the worst of famines. But for the clothes-moth it is quite in order. The hairs of fur, the fibres of wool, our own hair, and even the feathers of birds grow out of the living skin and consist of the same substance as the skin itself; that is, a material rich in nutritious albumen. It is solidified and chemically changed a little so that it cannot be attacked by our digestive juices, and thus cannot be dissolved in our stomachs. The speciality of the larvae of clothes-moths is that their digestive juices are slightly different in composition from ours, and are specially adapted to absorb this altered form of albumen, so that they are able to dissolve it. Thus it is that for them a meal of hair is just as nourishing as a steak is for us.

When human beings sit down to eat, it is regarded as bad manners to swallow chunks of food greedily and without chewing. It is also supposed to be unhealthy. In the animal world, among a great many species, the swallowing of entire chunks of unmasticated food is customary. Chewing is an exceptional occurrence. Among the vertebrates, for instance, we find that the mouths of fish, frogs, and snakes are furnished with teeth. Indeed they have many more teeth than human beings: but these teeth are sharp, pointed fangs, their needle-points turned backwards – they are not designed for mastication and are not used for this purpose at all. Their function is to prevent the escape of captured prey. When a snake has caught a frog, or when a pike has caught a fish, these cruel, hook-like teeth are very necessary to prevent the prey's escape. The 'Wels' (catfish), that huge pirate of European streams, has about ten thousand teeth in its jaws.

For the warm-blooded animals among the vertebrates – the birds and the mammals, including man – chewing is very important. Their food is the fuel for their bodies. To be able to maintain their high body temperatures, they have to refuel with ample nutriment, just as a stove is supplied with fuel. The more the food is pulverised by the teeth, the sooner it can afterwards be dissolved in the stomach and intestines through the action of the digestive juices, and the sooner refuelling of the heating system takes place. That is why the plant-eating animals in particular chew their rather indigestible forage so thoroughly.

But how does this apply to birds ? They also are warm-blooded, indeed they have an especially lively metabolism and their normal temperature is equal to that of a man suffering from the highest degree of fever. Yet they have horny, toothless beaks and, as most people have observed, fowl and pigeons swallow whole hard grain, which must be very difficult to digest. They too, however, pulverise their food mechanically and they do it even more thoroughly than human beings do. The naturalist Réaumur discovered this long ago. It was then still disputed whether digestion inside the stomach should be regarded as a mechanical or chemical process. Réaumur thought up a very neat experiment to settle this question one way or the other. He bought some large glass beads and inserted grains of oats into the holes. He reasoned that if digestion took place by chemical action the oats would dissolve, disappearing from the holes in the beads. If, on the other hand, the process was a mechanical one, then the grains of oats would be protected and would stay whole. He fed the oat-filled beads to his turkeys and waited expectantly for their reappearance. But he waited in vain. Nothing could be discovered in the droppings of the turkeys. He continued to search for the missing beads and by killing the turkeys at varying periods after they had been fed, he found that the beads had been ground to the finest glass powder in the birds' stomachs.

The stomach of a grain-eating bird is a food-grinding system. Its high efficiency has been indicated by the experiment just described. Its walls are extremely muscular and covered with a layer of harsh, horn-like substance. Grain-eating birds, furthermore, have the habit of swallowing small stones which operate in the stomach like mill-stones, crushing the contents very finely as the muscles of the stomach-walls contract powerfully. The contents are then pushed along into the intestines for the chemical part of the treatment. Grain-eating birds in fact chew their food very thoroughly, but they do so with their stomachs, and the stones which they swallow perform, basically, the work of the teeth they lack.

There are other ways of getting over the lack of teeth. For instance, living on liquid food. This is a very widely practised solution to the problem of meal preparation in the animal world. The flea which bites human beings and then sucks their blood, the butterfly which sips sugary juice from flowers with its proboscis, the humming-bird which, with its long beak, extracts the rich nectar from tropical flowers – none of these needs to worry about the processing of its nutritious liquids. It is a less well-known fact that many animals, indeed many very familiar ones, live off quite solid food and yet take it in as a liquid substance: they digest it before it enters their mouths. When, for instance, a spider has caught a fly in its intricately constructed web, it kills it with a poisonous bite and then spits a drop of digestive juice into the interior of the fly through the hole made by the bite. For this it is of great advantage to the spider that flies, like all insects, have a firm armour of skin enclosing the body as a shell encloses an egg. The digestive juice which the spider spits into the fly dissolves all the muscles and intestines, and this liquid cannot run out because the external armour encloses it. After a time the spider can drink the whole liquefied content, and only the empty armour remains.

Let us finally cast a glance into the world of deep-sea life, into the vast depths of the oceans where no light penetrates. There exists a great wealth of life here, small creatures of all kinds, including fish that carry their own small lanterns to illuminate the gloom of their environment. I shall select only one class of deep-sea creatures. Once again we approach the point of departure of our observations, namely human custom. The human housewife is in charge of the household. She takes care that the husband has enough to eat. This also applies to many of the deep-sea fish and – how perfect! – in some cases the wife not only makes herself responsible for the provision of food, she even eats for her husband! At a very early age the male seeks out a female. When he has found one, he bites firmly into her skin and grows into his wife so that they become one creature; he loses his eyes, and even his brain, living off the bloodstream of his wife.

Animal Flight and Human Flying Techniques

ERICH VON HOLST

The path which has taken human beings towards the mastery of the air is richly paved with errors and false conclusions – more so perhaps than any other field of human endeavour. Man's very earliest attempts at flight were linked with a false conclusion which, since it still seems to mesmerise everyone concerned with flight, I shall begin by analysing.

The inspiration of all man's attempts to leave the earth's surface and elevate himself into the blue quite certainly originated with man's daily contemplation of the flying creatures of the animal world. If he had not observed for centuries how birds sail into the vastness of the sky by beating their wings, he would hardly have hit upon the idea that such a thing was possible. As ground-dwelling creatures, we experience the air as something quite weightless, something that offers no resistance, something intangible, something, finally, which we would not readily trust to carry our weight.

But since birds have flown before our eyes ever since human thought originated, we have believed that we need only imitate what they are doing, once we have discovered how they do it. Small wonder that it has always been visually minded people, painters and sculptors, who have been especially captivated by the challenge of the problem – Leonardo, Goya, Arnold Böcklin, and others. But they were the victims of a delusion shared by every uninitiated observer. When one sees a large bird, a seagull or a stork, sailing along with quiet slow movements of the wings, the impression is automatically gained that the act requires no effort: the slower the beating of the wings the easier the act of flying appears to be. One is inclined to attribute greater expenditure of effort to a bird such as a pheasant that flaps along with rapid wing-beats. But in fact the exact opposite is true: the more slowly a bird moves its wings the more force it has to apply. We cannot know from personal experience that a slowly oscillating surface which glides forward through the air with great speed creates enormous power. We cannot easily imagine that for birds the air really has, as it were, wooden beams. Only careful measurements have taught us this, and they prove that flying with moving wings is by no means less exhausting, more energy-conserving, than flying with rigid wings pulled forwards by the movements of a propeller.

All this is a profound disappointment for those who imagined that human winged flight based on muscular power might be feasible. It was this hope that gave ever-new impetus to the exploration of bird flight: if only man knew how to execute the correct movements he too could fly, so it was thought. Today we do know all the correct movements: we are able to build 'artificial birds' which can lift themselves into the air exactly like living birds, fly about without losing their equilibrium, and land properly. The only thing we cannot do is mount these birds and propel them with the power of our arms or our legs, as if they were a kind of aerial bicycle. They need the driving-power of a motor. We human beings are much too weak to be able to carry our own weight by such means. Not only are our muscles too weak, but our metabolism is not sufficiently high-powered, our circulation is too slow, our hearts are too small and too weak, and our lungs do not permit us to take in oxygen fast enough. So the thought that one day we might leave our homes and mount an aircycle and pedal over the mountains and forests remains nothing but a beautiful dream.

I have mentioned that today we can build artificial birds which can perform as well as real ones. But how do those real birds move their wings, and why did it take us so long to find out how to imitate them, to discover the secrets of a bird's flight? Now that we have the right information it is easy to give the right answers. The reason is that there are no such secrets. The movements of a bird's wing are nothing more than an ideal adaptation to the qualities of the medium of flight, air. To the moving wing, air is nothing but a liquid – not a gas that can be compressed, but a flowing liquid of very low density. And so we find it easiest to understand the motions of flying when we start by thinking of fish swimming in water. Fish swim with sinuous movements. Either the whole body forms a wavy line, undulating from head to tail, as with the eel, or it is only the tail or perhaps only the pectoral fins which describe such a sinuous path, and continuously adapt their surface exactly to this path. Precisely the same procedure applies to all flying creatures: the tip of the wing describes an undulating path, up and down, while the body glides forward in a straight line; it is not a matter of the wing being swung up and down like a stiff and rigid plane. The wing adapts itself in the most finely balanced way to this sinuous path. When it beats down, its front edge inclines downwards, and when it beats upwards with the opposite movement the front edge is inclined upwards. Everything depends on the exactitude of this motor component. When we see with the naked eye a crow or a seagull flying even very close to us, the details of the movement are not perceptible. We see only the rise and fall, not the rotation, or more correctly the torsion of the wing around its own longitudinal axis. It was the slow-motion film that first clarified the details of this movement.

It is not correct to say, as is sometimes claimed, that a bird can hold itself up in the air because when it beats its wings down it compresses the air underneath it and then rests on this air cushion, and when it beats upwards it makes its wings small and brings them up again as quickly as possible. On the contrary, since the wing, in both beating up *and* beating down, adapts precisely to the sinuous path and glides through the liquid surrounding it, it can, both when beating upwards and when beating downwards, create an updraught which carries its weight in exactly the same way. If you observe the flight of a seagull or a stork closely, you will notice that the body of the bird glides forward on a straight course as if it were tied to the sky by an invisible string from above. It does not rise when its wings beat down, and it does not fall when the wings beat upwards. And, of course, exactly the same applies to artificial birds. The elegance of these flying movements, the aesthetic enjoyment to be gained from them, is a direct result of the precise adaptation of the wing movement. The first artificial birds I built did not move their wings with perfect adaptation and were thus not very beautiful to watch in flight. At first my aesthetic pleasure was disturbed; only later did technical knowledge identify the cause of my un-easiness and enable me to eliminate it. If the mechanics of a movement are perfectly adapted to the medium, or if the greatest economy of movement is combined with the highest degree of efficiency, the result will be a movement which is also highly satisfying aesthetically. This is a general rule which has validity not only for natural but also for artificial motor mechanisms.

I said just now that the old wish that we might fly by using wings activated by our own muscle power could never come true. The question naturally arises whether a bird's methods of flying have any relevance at all to human flight techniques, whether we can perhaps learn something in some other direction? I believe that we can now answer this question in the affirmative: we really *can* learn something from a bird's flight techniques, precisely because they are superior to the flight techniques of man in one decisive point: in what is called 'broad speed range'. I shall explain this in a little more detail.

Our typical modern aeroplanes are designed to achieve great speeds, but they cannot fly slowly. The more their speed capacity increases, the more problematic and hazardous become take-off and landing, in spite of all the technical aids. On the other hand we have in the helicopter an aircraft which can remain stationary in the air and which can take off and land anywhere. But it can attain only very low flying speeds. The normal aeroplane cannot fly slowly because it has rigid wings to carry it and is driven forward by a propeller or a jet. Only when it has reached a certain speed can the air current around the wings produce an up-draught which lifts the heavy weight of the aircraft. The helicopter on the other hand does not have rigid wings, but instead an air propeller rotating around a vertical axis which pulls upwards instead of forwards, and on which the weight of the aircraft hangs directly, so that high speeds in a horizontal direction become impossible. Flying creatures have no such problem since they do not have rigid wings. Their movable wings combine the function of load-bearing with that of forward drive, as required at any particular moment. A bird can both fly at top speed and slow down at will. It can also land and take off from any chosen point, with no forward velocity.

There exist natural experts in the art of flying on the spot, i.e. hovering; many insects belong to this category, as do humming-birds. The difference between forward flying and flying on the spot consists simply in the fact that in the two cases the wings are moved at different angles. They are nearly vertical in forward flying, that is they move downwards from above and then upwards again. In flying on the spot the wings are more or less horizontal, that is they move from behind forward and then back again. If the bird wants to fly slowly it moves its wings on an inclined plane, the wings moving from above and behind to below and in front. These differently angled planes of the wing-beat create differently directed aerodynamic forces. A horizontal plane creates air power vertically upwards: the bird is borne upwards, but does not move forward. And the more the plane of the wing-beat approaches the vertical, the more the forward driving force increases, and the more flying speed increases. All this may be easily demonstrated with artificial birds. A large artificial bird would be decisively superior to modern types of aircraft in one particular aspect: it would combine the advantages of the jet and the helicopter.

It would be technically quite possible to build a large motor-driven bird – but it would be far from simple. First of all, the body of the big, slow, wing-beating apparatus would necessarily perform oscillating movements itself, which might be disruptive. This problem could be dealt with if we were to take not the bird but the dragonfly as our prototype. Dragonflies, like most flying insects, have two wings on either side of their bodies and move these two pairs of wings in opposite directions: when the front pair of wings beats downwards the rear pair moves upwards, and vice versa. One pair of wings is therefore always ready to beat downwards, so that the body of an artificial dragonfly would not be prone to disruptive oscillations. But there is another more important difficulty which would have to be overcome. Technical investigations have shown time and again that the movement of *oscillating* masses is difficult to control; it would therefore be much more rational to plan a *rotating* movement for our model.

This would mean that each wing, instead of rising and falling, would rotate constantly in the same direction around the body, for instance moving down the right side of the body, then passing beneath it to rise again on the left side of the body, while the other wing of the pair would move in the opposite direction, with its downstroke on the left side of the body and its upstroke on the right side. This is in fact easily achieved and such a mechanised dragonfly, which would be able to remain stationary in the air and also reach the highest speeds which are possible today, would have two propellers which would move slowly in contrary directions around the body axis. Each of these two propeller blades, in exactly the manner of a bird's wing, would simultaneously support and propel forwards.

An Excursion through the Sensory World of Animals

SVEN DIJKGRAAF

Every animal perceives the external environment only through what its senses can find out about it. It lives in a world of its own, which is more or less distinct from that of other animals and that of human beings. Such distinctions are partly based on differences in construction of the sense organs; but they are primarily evoked by different modes of life. Flying, swimming, and nocturnal animals, for instance, face quite different conditions from those of man, who lives on the ground and is adapted to daytime activity. It is, therefore, hardly surprising that study of the efficiency of animal senses often reveals capacities that appear uncanny to the human mind. Let us take a brief excursion through the world of animal sense-perception, looking closely at certain special capabilities.

Let us first of all take a creature known to everyone, the honey-bee. The astonishing discoveries made by the Munich zoologist, Karl von Frisch, in his investigations of the so-called 'language' of bees, excited both specialist circles and the general public, and exercised a stimulating influence over other fields of investigation. We shall refer to them briefly here.

Bees are social creatures: they live in communities, and their well-ordered communal life presupposes some form of communication between individual bees in the hive. It has long been known that a transmission of information concerning food does occur in bees. If a bee finds a rich food supply, it will signal the fact to its companions on returning to the hive, and they will go in increasing numbers to the food supply in order to take part in collecting it. Many kinds of ants behave in a similar fashion, showing each other the way by marking their tracks with scent which they exude. With bees this is not so simple, since their sources of food are plants and flowers reached by flying through the air, where it is hardly possible to lay a reliable trail of scent. Even so, scent plays an important part in their system of communications.

It has to be demonstrated that when the alerted bees swarm out of the hive they search especially for the scent of the food-source which has just been discovered. The bee which discovered it carries this scent home not only in its body-hairs, but also – in an even more effective manner – in the nourishment it has taken in, in the contents of the honey sac which will be regurgitated in the hive for the benefit of the community.

Such a form of communication would hardly be sufficient if the feeding site were a long way from the hive; yet alerted bees may arrive at the site from several miles away. In fact, bees tell one another not only *what* they should search for but also *where* they will find it. The manner in which they communicate is one of the most exciting biological phenomena to be discovered for a long time.

The homing bee executes a very special movement on the vertical honeycomb, the so-called tail-wagging dance, during which it runs continuously round in tight semicircles, first in one direction and then in the opposite; these semicircles are connected by a straight line which the bee will follow, always in the same direction, while wagging its tail. The frequency of these tail-wagging runs shows the distance from the hive to the source of food: they decrease from about forty runs per minute when the distance is in the region of one hundred yards away to about ten runs per minute when it is about two miles away.

But the direction in which the food-source lies is also communicated by means of the tail-wagging run. The key to the code is this: if the dance on the comb points vertically upwards, then the food-source lies in a direct line from the hive in the direction of the sun. If the direction of the dance is vertically downwards, then the direction of the food-source will be the opposite of that of the sun. If the direction of the dance deviates about sixty degrees to the left of the vertical, then the alerted bees have only to keep sixty degrees to the left of the sun in order to fly in the exact direction of the food-source, and so on. Therefore the position of the food-source in relation to the position of the sun is translated into the appropriate angle of the direction of the dance with respect to the vertical. It has been found that this association between two distinct sensory fields in animals, which seems so strange to us, is by no means unique to bees. Rudiments of the same ability have been found in ants, as well as in a beetle species.

One important discovery often leads to others. Thus the old mystery of how birds orient themselves over enormous distances has recently moved much nearer to its solution.

The behaviour of many migratory birds has long demonstrated the existence of special abilities for orientation. Often vast distances, covering deserts and oceans, have to be traversed in a straight line. Migratory birds have been transported at right angles to the direction of their migratory flight and then released, and these experiments have proved that at least young inexperienced birds actually follow a definite compass direction, quite independently of the landscape below them. Many experiments have been made in which birds have been taken from their nests and then released elsewhere to fly over territory unknown to them. These experiments have yielded further proof of special capacities for orientation. In most cases half to three-quarters of the birds displaced have found their way home, some of them relatively quickly, even over distances as great as several hundred miles.

In itself this would not demonstrate an ability to return home in an oriented manner; even if released birds were to search around aimlessly, the chances are that a proportion would somehow arrive in familiar territory and thus find their way home. It is necessary to know *how* birds fly home, and to this end they must be followed in their flight. This has been done in two different ways. First, by observation from a slow-flying aircraft such as a helicopter. The initial results seemed to indicate nothing but random searching in all directions. But the bird species selected was not really suitable for the experiments because the birds were typical gliders, that is birds which rely on ascending currents of air in starting their flight. This factor might have considerably influenced the starting direction of their flight.

Quite different results were obtained from observations made from aircraft on carrier pigeons which had been released in foreign territory. These birds flew home in a direct line. Two investigators, Kramer in Germany and Matthews in England, have made experiments with carrier pigeons which have produced conclusive evidence on the effects of transport away from home. The conditions under which the experiments were conducted were strictly controlled. Binoculars were used to observe as far as possible the direction in which the pigeons started to travel after they had been released in an unfamiliar spot. Several important facts emerged from these experiments.

In the first place, it was demonstrated that carrier pigeons are able to return to their base in a straight line from unfamiliar territory. This was found to be so even when the birds had had no training in flying over long distances. Secondly, it was found that the correct direction for home was chosen immediately upon take-off; the birds did not start off by circling round, and therefore had no opportunity to take their bearings from any available gradient. Finally, the pigeons were transported at right angles to a line of flight along which they had been trained to return home from a definite point of the compass, and released. The majority chose their customary compass direction from the point of release. These birds did not reach home, or arrived there only after a long detour flight. But some birds chose the right direction for home immediately they were released. From this experiment it may be assumed that there are two different mechanisms working in the orientation system of these birds. One is the tendency and the ability to follow a certain compass direction, the other is the ability to determine the position of the home base from any randomly selected point, for which task a compass would be inadequate.

The first ability is based on use of the sun as an orientation mark. Kramer's experiments in training starlings, carrier pigeons, and other birds have shown that these birds have an innate capacity for exact calculation of the movements of the sun during the course of the day, while they are taking their bearings from the sun. They would appear to have a built-in clock – as have bees and a number of other creatures.

61

The carrier pigeon's second faculty, that of finding its way home in a direct line from an arbitrary spot, remains a mystery. It could perhaps theoretically be explained on the basis of observation of the sun alone; that is assuming that the bird observes not only the position of the sun but also its course. Whether this hypothesis is correct is still a matter of dispute.

Both bees and birds are creatures with very good eyesight. Animals whose eyesight is bad or limited in use possess other compensatory sensory faculties. One example is the ability of fish and bats to detect distant objects by mechanical means. Fish are able to perceive moving objects – prey or approaching predators – some distance away without tactile contact. Distant movement receptors are situated along the lateral line, a system of special tactile sense organs in the outer skin of aquatic vertebrates. These receptors are capable of detecting the minute water movements which accompany every moving object underwater.

Some years ago an English zoologist made the interesting observation that certain tropical fish perpetually emit weak electric impulses. In this manner they create an electrically charged field around themselves. Every disturbance of that field will be accurately sensed by the fish – for instance the presence of a potential prey whose body conducts electricity much more efficiently than the fresh water in which it lives. This electrically operated distant perception mechanism assists location and capture of prey. When such fish live in the vicinity of human settlements, metal objects of all kinds can often be found in their stomachs. These have been swallowed in mistake for prey, since they too are conductors of electricity.

Bats, too, are capable of perceiving objects from a distance without being able to see them. The fact that these creatures do not rely on their eyes to avoid obstacles in their path of flight has been known since 1793, the date of Spallanzani's discovery. But it was some time before we discovered which sense organ had been substituted for the eye. Today we know that in contrast to the fish, bats do not utilise a highly developed sense of touch, but perceive objects with their ears. Whether crawling or flying, they emit incessant sound-signals which are projected forwards, and they recognise objects by the reflected echo of these sounds. In this fashion bats in flight are not only able to perceive obstacles in their path but also to spot their prey (night-flying insects).

The sounds which bats transmit to orient themselves are composed of very short sound pulses of high frequency. The high frequency (about fifty thousand cycles per second) is advantageous, because high sound frequency is associated with a short wave-length. The wave-length of the bat's sound measures about 7 mm. Because of this, even very small and narrow objects clearly echo the transmitted orientation sounds. With deeper tones and greater wave-length this would not occur. It has been proved experimentally that bats can perceive a cord down to 1 mm. in diameter. Any thinner structures fail to reflect the sounds emitted by bats, so that a length of cotton, for instance, will not be perceived. This is precisely what inspires the fear which women have that bats might get caught in their hair. This would be at least as upsetting for the bat as for the woman: the bat is quite unable to sense the hair and suddenly finds itself caught in a net. It will certainly try to free itself as quickly as possible – but let any woman be warned not to grab at the little creature in a panic, otherwise she will be made to feel its sharp teeth. Not that the bat is a malevolent creature, but in a state of panic it will defend itself against a supposed enemy. On the other hand, the woolly hair of the moth (the bat's most important prey) offers protection against its deadly enemy, swallowing up the sound-pulses.

While most European bats transmit their orientation sounds through their mouths, there are two species which differ in this respect. The horseshoe bats transmit sound through their nostrils. These species are far more sensitive than other bats, which can only perceive even quite large objects, such as the wall of a room, at a distance of about a yard. The horseshoe bats hear objects up to six or seven yards away. The so-called tropical flying foxes or fruit bats, whose sound-orientation has been investigated by the German zoologist Moehres, feed not on insects but on fruit. It has been found that the large species depend entirely on their well developed eyes: they do not send out sounds and in absolute darkness they cannot avoid obstacles. On the other hand, the small fruit bats, apart from very good eyesight, also possess the echo apparatus. In their case the sound is transmitted through the nostrils, as with the horseshoe bat.

The Operational Limits of Animal Sense Organs

HANSJOCHEM AUTRUM

The sense organs are the doors of perception through which we learn about our environment and what takes place in it. We test the world around us by taking in samples from it through our sense organs. Through our nose we get a trace of smell substances, with our eyes a small portion of the light which comes from the sun or artificial sources and from reflecting surfaces, while our ears take in part of the energy produced by sound waves which flow around us in space.

The smaller the quantities which suffice to obtain a response from the sense organs, the more sensitive the organs and therefore the more precise will be the information they give us about the nature of our environment. How sensitive are the most highly developed human and animal sense organs, and what can they achieve?

Let us begin with the eye. From what distance can we see the light from a battery-operated pocket torch in the dark? We must arrange some controls so that we can be sure of ascertaining the maximum possible distance. The night would have to be quite black; no foreign source of light should dazzle or distract us and we should have to accustom our eyes to the darkness for some time beforehand, say about half an hour, so that they reached their highest degree of sensitivity. If it were possible for the experiment to be conducted under these conditions, then we could see the bulb, though only just, from a distance of about six hundred miles.

From the brightness of the torch, its distance from the eye and the size of the pupils which let the light through, we can calculate how little light the eye needs to be able simply to provide the information 'light'. Calculation shows that at the threshold of vision the eye needs a light energy of $5 \cdot 10^{-17}$ watt.

Everybody must be familiar with the word 'watt'. We all know forty-watt bulbs, which are not very bright; the surface provided by five watts is approximately one-eighth of that of a forty-watt bulb. And $5 \cdot 10^{-17}$ watts – that is, five watts divided by one followed by seventeen noughts? A minute amount of light which I find as impossible to visualise as the reader will. Let us therefore try to translate this measurement into something a little more meaningful. If I switch on an electric stove which uses 1 kW and leave it on for one hour, then it will have used 1 kWh (kilowatt-hour), which costs, let us say, 11 pfennigs. I can burn a small bulb which uses only one watt for one thousand hours for the same money, since there are one thousand watts in 1 kW. How long must my eye absorb the smallest amount of light which can still be perceived – $5 \cdot 10^{-17}$ watt, so that the amount of light absorbed would similarly cost 11 pfennigs? A simple calculation shows that two million times one thousand million years are required. How long a time is that? The physicists think that the cosmos – not just the earth – has existed for only two thousand million years. Therefore, an eye which since the beginning of the world had continuously used up the threshold quantity of light energy would by now have received energy worth only 1/100 000 pfennigs.

By no means all human and animal sense organs which have been investigated are developed to such a high degree of sensitivity as the human eye, but in the most sensitive among them, for instance the human ear and the ear of the great green bush-cricket, the threshold of sound perception is very low indeed. Another sense organ which is equally sensitive exists in insects to register vibrations.

This organ is very interesting in many respects. To begin with, many insects are about ten thousand times more sensitive to vibrations and shocks than human beings. Astonishing also is the small scale of the vibrations which can be felt by many insects. A movement of half a hundred millionth of a millimetre can be perceived. Let us try to make this size meaningful. The radius of an atom of hydrogen is twenty-five times as large as the smallest vibrations which a grasshopper can perceive. Or let us multiply all dimensions a hundred million times. A human being would then be one hundred and six thousand miles tall, which means that he would reach half-way to the moon. Our two-inch long grasshopper would be two and a half thousand miles long, which means that it would extend from the North Cape to Sicily. Its minimum threshold of vibration perception would then be only half a millimetre! With these comparative figures in mind, it is understandable that a cricket stops singing as soon as one tries to creep up to it, however carefully one approaches. The insect perceives the quietest of footfalls from a distance and retreats into its hole in the ground.

Incidentally, if one reduces the measurements of light, sound and vibration energy to a common denominator (which is physically possible), it is found that the peaks of performance of the different sense organs are of about the same order of magnitude.

The above figures are so staggeringly small that it may well be asked whether they represent the limits of possible performance, or whether there could be sense organs with a still higher degree of sensitivity. A comparison with the most sensitive kinds of apparatus used in physics shows first of all that, in general terms, they cannot surpass the achievements of the sense organs of animals. One of the most sensitive physical receptors for wave-radiation is a good radio receiving set, which responds to electromagnetic waves with an energy of about 10^{-17} watt. It is thus exactly as sensitive as is the human eye to light or the human ear to sound waves or the special organs of insects to vibrations.

Here lies an absolute limit, not only for the instruments which we use to measure physical quantities but also for sense organs. We know that a really good, highly sensitive radio receiver makes a faint noise. If it is particularly required to provide good transmission of sounds of the highest frequency, then the noise cannot be eliminated: this is part of the nature of the set. The electro-magnetic fields of the transmitter affect the radio-wave receiving set by pushing the mobile electrons in the aerial to-and-fro. On the other hand, the electrons themselves possess, by their very nature, a certain volatility, and there are therefore, purely incidentally, sometimes a few more and sometimes a few less of them at the intake of the receiver. These autonomous movements of the electrons, which are independent of the transmitter, are expressed through crackling noises. Exactly the same phenomenon occurs in hearing. Perception of sound means that periodic variations of air pressure are being received. The air pressure itself is produced by air molecules constantly bouncing against adjacent surfaces, performing perpetual dancing movements. As a result, they also strike the ear-drum, and it is in the nature of air pressure that sometimes more and sometimes fewer molecules collide with the ear membrane. These inevitable fluctuations in the numbers of colliding molecules create small fluctuations of pressure on the ear-drum. The ear would perceive these as a constant crackling if it were just a little more sensitive than it actually is. There would be no advantage at all in the ear being more sensitive; it already achieves as much as is physically possible.

The eye also has an absolute limit to its sensitivity. Light actually consists of single, very small light flashes, the elemental processes or light quanta. Physicists have shown that these units cannot in any way be reduced in size: less than a light quantum cannot emerge from a source of light, still less could it be absorbed by the eye. These indivisible light quanta are very small. Forty to fifty of them are needed to stimulate the eye of a human being or an animal. They correspond to the above-mentioned light energy of $5 \cdot 10^{-17}$ watt. But not all the quanta which fall into the eye reach the visual receptors in the retina at the back of the eye. A proportion will be reflected by the cornea, others will be retained in the lens and the viscous medium in the eye; only about ten to thirty reach the visual cells. These ten to thirty quanta do not fall on one single cell but are distributed over an area of about one hundred cells. Each cell thus receives probably only about one quantum, and therefore responds to what is physically the minimum possible quantity of light energy. One quantum is enough to evoke a stimulus. The single visual cell therefore cannot be any more sensitive than it is already, for purely physical reasons. The capabilities of our sense organs are indeed almost unbelievable.

It might be claimed that, if the visual cells are really so sensitive, we should be able to see every star, even the weakest, because even this cannot transmit to our eyes less than a single quantum of light energy; and the visual cells, as we have seen, react to the absorption of one light quantum. And yet we see the stars only when they have a definite degree of brightness; that is, when they transmit to our eyes a fixed number of light quanta within a certain time limit. There are a number of factors which explain this apparent contradiction. One of these is that, while on the one hand the visual cells themselves are as sensitive as it is possible for them to be, and are therefore stimulated by a single quantum, on the other hand *our nervous system as a whole* permits a sensation of light only when, inside a certain very limited period of time, several impulses (2–5) are transmitted to the central nervous system from the same cell or from neighbouring cells. This arrangement can be regarded as a security measure. With a single physical process such as the absorption of one light quantum in the visual purple, it could never be certain that it had not happened by accident, that is by some process other than the impact of light. The organism protects itself against such unpredictability of single physical elementary processes, which could come about spontaneously without any external cause, by transmitting a signal to a higher centre only when a second impulse of the same kind is received not too long after the first.

If we ask what are the limits of capacity of animal sense organs, and in particular what are the smallest amounts of stimulus energy that may be perceived, we can say this. Many sense organs, not only those of human beings, are as sensitive as is physically possible. The limits of their capacity are due in the first place to the existence of a minimum size of energy unit, the quantum; in the second place they lie where perception would move into the realm of chance and uncertainty because of the existence of statistical fluctuations.

Finally, let us consider quite a different limitation to the capacities of sense organs – the natural inertia of every instrument of measurement and of every sense organ. If phases of light, darkness and light follow one another too rapidly, then we do not see the darkness in between the two phases of light. The cinema makes use of this phenomenon: if a sufficient number of pictures is projected per second, the film ceases to flicker. Man can perceive as a flicker at most about twenty to thirty such light flashes per second. If there are more, the inertia of the eye will prevent discrimination between light and darkness. However, some insects have a far higher capacity than man to discriminate between light stimuli following one another in rapid succession: bees and bumble-bees, dragonflies and house-flies, all fast flyers, perceive two hundred and fifty light impulses per second – even, in favourable circumstances, three hundred or more – as a flicker.

Were a cinema show to be set up for bees, at least ten times as many pictures would have to be projected as for human beings, i.e. two hundred and fifty or more per second, instead of the twenty-four customary in the cinema. What is the significance of this astonishing speed of perception? If one assesses the visual acuity of the bee (that is, the ability to discriminate between adjacent objects) from the anatomical structure of its eyes, then bees see extraordinarily badly: they have at most only one-eightieth of the acuity of human vision. In spite of this, they find themselves very much at home in their surroundings. They do not see surrounding objects when they are at rest, as human beings do; but they do recognise them when they are in flight. To our human eyes, which are too insensitive to separate stimuli which follow one another in rapid succession, fast movement blurs our surroundings – for instance when we pass close to houses or trees while travelling by train. With flying insects, it is the other way round: their eyes take in ten times as many impressions as ours do in the same space of time. They see well only when they are moving at sufficient speed past an object.

Our eyes see well when we are stationary, but are slow to respond. The eyes of a bee see badly when it is stationary, but respond very quickly. In this way, the limits imposed by structure are compensated by other means produced by the inventiveness of nature, so that by and large comparably high performance may be achieved in quite different ways.

The Physiologist and his Experimental Animals

ERICH VON HOLST

Strange to say, even today scientists can still quibble about what the term physiology really means. The pleasant phrase that it is 'the study of life' is one view, while the cynical remark that it is 'the study of dead frogs' represents the other extreme in a series of possible definitions. Whatever one may conclude, it can be stated with certainty that the physiologist always deals with living creatures, that is, those which are at least alive *before* he begins his study. For it lies in the nature of research into the hidden processes of life that it is often impossible to advance except through a surgical operation, or some other intervention which will alter the normal functional equilibrium. Such research leads to advance in knowledge on the one hand, but it also makes a sick animal out of a healthy one, and by no means infrequently leaves a corpse.

How does the research worker go about his job? What methods are available to him? How far must he remain aware of the fact that there is a vast difference between dealing with living organisms and with lifeless structures in seeking to understand their internal mechanisms? These are questions which not only concern the intellect but inevitably the emotions. Whenever we see living creatures, we become aware of their feelings of pain and pleasure, and are stimulated to participate in them. Of course, this applies in very varying degrees according to the kind of creature we are contemplating, because we are inclined to see any living creature as *to a greater or lesser degree* 'living'. To most ordinary observers, a snail seems to be less 'alive' than a lizard, and a worm less than a bee. And most ordinary onlookers are less moved when they see a frog killed by a car than when they see a song-bird run over. We are accordingly most moved by the sight of warm-blooded animals which are closely related to us – the birds and the mammals.

The differences in man's attitudes towards animals depend even more on the observer than on the animal observed. There are, everywhere, human beings to whom animals are nothing more than so much usable material. The attitude of whole nations to animals can vary greatly – even within Europe. I still remember the depression I felt when staying as a guest twenty years ago in an institute abroad; I discovered one day in a pile of refuse several discarded rabbits which were still alive. Their urethras had been tied off, and they were lying about, twitching in the last convulsive fits of slowly advancing self-poisoning. In that particular country one would presumably have protested in vain against unnecessary cruelty to animals. In Germany, such coarseness would (I hope) be scarcely possible; still less so in England or Holland. At least, it would be decried by all scientists, and the offence would be punishable.

But let us go back to the starting-point of our reflections. What does the physiologist actually do with his experimental animal? The answer is that there are basically two possibilities, because there are two contrasting methods of investigating the ways in which life functions. One of these methods concentrates on the understanding of a single action. In this method, the study will be of *the* contraction of muscles, *the* transmission of impulses by a nerve, *the* secretion of a gland. This kind of physiology has a very long history and the single bricks which it collects to build its edifice of scientific knowledge do indeed add up to something like 'the study of dead animals', because in all such cases the animal as a whole is first killed, either by the administration of an anaesthetic or by some other painless method. From the corpse the researcher takes the still beating heart, the still conducting nerve, or the still light-sensitive eye – in each instance a surviving part of the living organism which has just been destroyed. The physiologist can, of course, deal as he likes with such isolated organs as will nevertheless continue to function for a while. He can expose them to cold and warm temperatures, or to chemicals; he can stimulate them electrically, infuse or withhold nutrients and record all resultant activity.

But there is quite a different way of researching into the processes of life: not by reducing everything to its smallest components, but by leaving the whole as much as possible intact and experimenting only by altering the external circumstances and then observing the creature's general behaviour. Experiments of this kind are generally conducted so humanely that the experimental animal is not even aware that it is the object of an experiment. In this case the experiment is particularly elegant and fruitful. And no blood need flow.

I should like to explain the basic difference between these two methods of research, with the help of an example. Let us inquire, for instance, how the balancing organ hidden in the skull, the so-called labyrinth, functions and how it can be investigated. A physiologist of the first kind will proceed by first killing a suitable subject as humanely as possible; in this case a fish might be chosen. Then the labyrinth will be dissected out and placed in a special apparatus, where it will survive for a few hours. Recordings will be made during this time with the help of a complicated apparatus for registering the electrical responses to stimuli of the various sense-elements of the labyrinth when it is in a normal position, when its position is inclined, and when rotated. This tells us how the isolated organ responds, but we do not know how the whole animal, with such an apparatus for registering movements built into its body, responds. We do not know what becomes of the sensory messages which come from the labyrinth, how they are computed in the intact nervous system, and what kind of behaviour they cause the animal to adopt.

This is where the physiologist of the second kind comes in. He will develop an elaborate method which will lead a normal healthy fish to demonstrate to the observer how it responds as a whole to changes in its position. For instance, the fish may be acclimatised to a small cage in a tank, through which water is pumped in a particular direction, so that the fish is orientated against the current as if it were in a normal stream. Many fish have the habit of turning their backs to the light. Accordingly the fish may be illuminated through a lateral window in the tank so that, according to the light intensity, it will lie on its side at a greater or lesser angle. The current of water may also be directed so that, instead of coming horizontally from the front, it flows through the cage at an angle, from above or below. The fish, if swimming against the stream, would consequently point its nose upwards or downwards. In this way the fish adopts different positions without any direct constraint and can thus reveal its normal behaviour to the observer. Such studies, *together with* those conducted by physiologists on the isolated labyrinth, will yield a complete picture.

It will be seen from this example that the two methods of physiological research call for *different types* of research worker. An 'organ physiologist' must be able to master surgical techniques and also devise methods of using the available apparatus for recording physical and chemical measurements. A knowledge of the animal in its normal habitat would be of little value to him. On the other hand, anyone who is engaged in the physiology of the whole animal – we shall call him a 'system physiologist', because he has the entire system before him – must be familiar with his subject in its natural environment and under natural conditions, or he will never find useful techniques for eliciting precise responses, given voluntarily and without coercion. One really cannot tie an animal down on a board, subject it to certain stimuli and then expect its responses to be normal. Its defence mechanisms and attempts to free itself, as well as fear and general apathy, will distort the results of any investigation.

Many physiologists have successfully carried out research on the responses of constrained dogs; but such a procedure characteristically leads to the appearance of severe nervous disturbances. There is only one research subject which can exhibit reasonably appropriate physiological responses when fettered, and that is man. He alone has some understanding of the situation and can therefore voluntarily submit to whatever discomforts might be imposed on him.

If we want to distinguish the two types of physiologist by their attitude towards living animals, then we can safely say that the first does not have any specific attitude at all; he only applies physics and chemistry to research on 'surviving' organs or their parts. The organism *as a whole* emerges only later as a conceptual construction. The other kind of physiologist must, by contrast, be a connoisseur of animals, and his knowledge of animals stems in the early stages from handling and becoming familiar with them. In this way there develops an ability which reaches perfection only in certain individuals who have that rare talent we might call 'animal sense', as one speaks of certain people as having 'horse sense'.

It is thus safe to assume that in 'system physiology' the scientific results depend directly on the insight of the investigator into the special life requirements of the animal species which is the subject of research.

An interesting result that has arisen from 'system' research is the predictability of behaviour. Somebody who can 'read' other people so accurately that, by putting himself in their place, he can predict what they are going to do and adapt himself to it, is said to be 'a good judge of human nature'. The connoisseur of animals is such a person, whose 'animal sense' tells him what his subject feels and therefore how it is going to react. But why should this faculty be so important? The sciences concerned with life processes have repeatedly demonstrated their immense complexity within living organisms, so that they can scarcely be comprehended in their entirety. For this reason, some physiologists conclude that the only course is to isolate the many functional components and explore each one separately; in short, to follow the path of 'organ physiology'. In the face of such a thesis, 'system physiology' has no easy time. It must demonstrate that, by means of its specialised methods, it can produce precise results, even without a knowledge of all individual components. In science, this means nothing less than the ability to make *predictions* in given situations as to what kind of behaviour is to be expected.

In comparison with the animal connoisseurs in this field, I am unfortunately only a poor relation – and yet I did at least once succeed in convincingly predicting one particular phenomenon. This took place some years ago during an academic meeting. I had been asked to read an experimental paper on the functions of equilibrium in animals, and I had prepared some experiments with fish such as I have described above, with fish swimming in small cages against a current of water. As I had expected, it was objected that such experiments on free-moving, intact animals could hardly yield unequivocal results: animals, like human beings, were likely to do sometimes one thing, sometimes another. I offered to prove that this was wrong. I asked those present, one after the other, to observe one particular fish through a glass window in the tank. They were able to see that the fish did indeed swim against the current, with its nose pointing towards whoever was watching. I maintained that the fish would, however, turn round and present its rear to the particular gentleman who had just expressed his doubts. And so it happened. My explanation that the gentleman wore glasses, and that my fish had an antipathy to spectacles, was – to be honest – not quite true. A true animal connoisseur would have guessed the truth quickly enough. He would have seen that the fish in question belonged to a species in which the mimicry posture requires that the tail should be pointed directly towards any threat of danger. In this position, the shape and colouring of the fish's body gives the impression of a leaf. On this occasion, the danger which triggered off the protective behaviour consisted in the thick lenses of the objector's horn-rimmed spectacles, which presented the fish with an illusion of enormous eyes observing it. It is a general rule in animal life that large, staring eyes are taken to mean danger. It was thus predictable that the fish would turn its back on the man wearing spectacles.

On the whole, with the advance of physiological science, the dominance of 'organ physiology' is comparatively decreasing as that of 'system physiology' increases. Thus the number of scientists who impose stricter standards upon themselves in the treatment of animals also grows constantly larger. These standards are stricter than any which could be embodied in any law designed for the protection of animals.

The Communications Network of
the Human Body

HANSJOCHEM AUTRUM

If I want to read a newspaper, I reach out for it with my hand.
The muscles in my hand receive a command. They will move
accordingly and I myself can feel what movements are being
performed. Then the image of the print is seen by my eyes and
my eyes report back what they see. A constant stream of signals
and messages runs from the sense organs to the main centres and
from there to the muscles. We are conscious only of a small
proportion of these signals. The human body possesses seven
hundred and fifty-two muscles, not counting those tiny ones
which are located under the body hairs and cause goose pimples
to rise. All these muscles are connected to nerves, the purpose of
which it is to move the muscles: most of these muscles contain
sense organs which report back what the muscle does at any given
moment, how strongly it contracts, how much it is tensed, etc.

The network of communications in the human body operates,
therefore, through four different components: the sense organs
which emit the signals; the nerves which conduct these signals;
the brain, the central station which both sends out its own
commands and receives, interprets and passes on messages; and
finally the muscles, which carry out the commands of the brain.
We do not know all the properties of any one of these organs.
One process, for instance, which remains entirely obscure is the
way in which the brain stores messages received. The brain not
only represents a switchboard; it is also a filing system for our
experiences and, last but not least, for our inherited information.

I shall describe what we do know about the transmission of
messages, taking the eye as an example. In the retina of the eye
there are visual cells which are sensitive to light, like the emul-
sion on a photographic plate. Indeed, there are similarities
between the visual cells and light-sensitive emulsions, especially

in the physicochemical processes of vision. Of course there is no silver bromide in the eye, but there is one, or perhaps several, pigments which have a low resistance to light. This very low light-resistance is essential: the light alters these pigments and their decomposition causes the signal 'light' to be recorded in the visual cells. In the language of communications technology it might be said that we know the button which is pressed by light when it produces a signal in the eye. But we do not know how this lever functions in detail. Yet we are quite familiar with a process which takes place afterwards: the visual cell responds to the alteration of the pigment with a small electric impulse. The strength of this signal is dependent on the brightness of the light; but it never spreads much farther than a millimetre.

How does the message that light has fallen into the eye reach the brain? The nerve cells adjoining the visual cells work with astonishing simplicity. While the morse alphabet uses two different signs, dots and dashes, the visual nerve cells of animals and human beings use only one signal: short impulses which all have the same duration, the same strength, and are conducted along the nerve fibre at the same speed.

Yet the content of the transmitted messages is extremely variable. Every characteristic of the images we see has to be communicated. Our brain learns that we are dealing with light of a particular colour and intensity, and that it has impinged upon a particular spot on the retina, from the particular nerve fibres conducting the signals from the eye. The brightness of the light is indicated by the frequency of the signals: the brighter the light, the more numerous the signals – in the dimmest light there will be only a few, perhaps two or three per second; bright sunlight fires volleys of them containing from three hundred to four hundred impulses per second. No more than about ten thousand impulses per second can be conducted by a nerve fibre. In all cases the impulses are exactly identical.

More complicated, and in its way most remarkable, is the eye's method of transmitting colour-signals. The human eye can discriminate an incredible number of colour differences, probably more than half a million. In about 1750, during its greatest period, the Paris tapestry factory of Gobelin used around twelve thousand differently dyed threads for the weaving of their wall tapestries. By contrast, modern techniques of colour reproduction in books and films require only three, at most four, colours, since the others can be produced by mixing. Similarly, our eyes have only a few (probably only three) kinds of colour-sensitive visual cells, one type responding most strongly to red light, the second to blue-green light, and the third to violet light. From the varying proportional mixtures of these simple colour-responses, we reconstruct the entire range of colours we perceive.

More precise details about these processes have been recently learned from investigations of signals in the particularly large optical nerve cells of frogs and cats. It was found, rather surprisingly, that the visual cells are more numerous than the nerve fibres. This means that the same fibre must transmit different colour-signals. One must bear in mind the fact that there is only one kind of signal and that its frequency is already reserved for the transmission of intensity. The solution to this communications problem is amazing: every kind of colour-sensitive visual cell has its own latency of transmission following the impact of light. First come the signals from those cells which are sensitive to red, then from those which are sensitive to blue-green, and finally from those sensitive to violet.

An analogy will help to clarify the process. Imagine you are fixing a date with three friends, and you arrange that the first person will telephone between ten and eleven, the second between eleven and twelve, and the last between twelve and one. In this way, you know before you lift the receiver who is going to be at the other end of the line. In the case of the eye the interval of time, which is the basis of communication between visual cells and brain, is much shorter: a fraction of a tenth of a second.

So we can see that the entire transmission of messages through the nervous system is always operated in the same fundamental manner with a single form of signal consisting of short impulses, each lasting roughly one-thousandth of a second. Everything that we see, hear, taste, smell, feel, all consciously given orders to the muscles, all the countless control messages given to the heart and the stomach, to glands and blood vessels, all these use a single cipher – the invariable nerve impulse. Specific connections, frequencies per second, and temporal groupings are the clues to coding and decoding of messages.

I have explained how the visual cell produces a weak electric impulse when light falls upon it. It may be asked why this potential is not transmitted directly through the nerve fibres to the brain, rather as we conduct the potential of our electric generating stations to light bulbs, etc., by way of cables. Nerve fibres have a resistance a million times higher than that of electric cables, so that there is no possibility of a direct transference of potential. Rather, it is the nerve fibres themselves which produce electric potentials at every point: they resemble a long and extremely fine chain of single electric batteries. This miracle is wrapped in a covering not much thicker than a millionth of a centimetre, composed of a superb insulating material. Insulation is especially necessary because the covering, or membrane, is maintained at a potential of about one-tenth of a volt by the nerve fibres. One-tenth of a volt is very high for a battery of such minute dimensions; if we translate this into terms which we can understand, we find that this means that over a distance of only one centimetre there is a potential of one hundred thousand volts. When the covering of the nerve fibres is exposed to an external potential – for instance, one coming from the visual cell – then the covering changes, losing its insulating capacity in the region of the visual cell. At first there will be a small short-circuit in the adjacent battery, then in the next one, and so on, and in this way a wave of short-circuits runs over the entire series of batteries in the fibre at a speed of about one hundred metres per second. Immediately afterwards, the nerve fibres reconstruct their covering and recharge their electrical batteries. Both short-circuit and recharging take about a thousandth of a second; the fibre is then ready to conduct a new impulse. As we have seen, each fibre has the capacity of conducting up to ten thousand impulses per second.

Now we know how signals are generated in the eye and conducted along the optic nerve. The rest of the sense organs function on similar lines. But, how, for instance, do the signals originate which are sent out by the central nervous system to the muscles? It was once thought that the living organism could be understood as a kind of machine, to be compared with a tele-phone exchange which simply passes on messages which have been received from elsewhere. It is true that such simple pro-cesses as a message arriving and a response immediately follow-ing do exist in the human body. If I strike the tendon below my knee-cap with the edge of my hand or with a light hammer, my foot will jerk upwards: the blow pulls at the tendon, sense organs report this to the central nervous system, the message is at once transmitted to the leg muscle and the leg muscle moves. But circumstances are seldom so simple. On the contrary, we know that the central nervous system is not merely a switchboard, still less a machine which produces cigarettes when money is placed in the slot. The central nervous system produces impulses all the time; it is constantly sending out signals of the most varied kinds; it is perpetually active and alert. A proportion of these signals are transmitted directly to the receivers – for example, to the muscles or other centres – keeping these in a state of per-manent readiness. If, then, a signal arrives from outside the body the constant stream of impulses can be modified, reinforced, or diminished. There are also complicated sequences of signals, comparable to sealed orders, built into our central nervous system, latent but ever-ready. These sequences can only function when the seal is broken by a cue – or what the psychologist calls a 'key stimulus'. This is the sphere of instinctive behaviour patterns. A simple example is the swallowing of a morsel of food: once the food has passed far enough into the mouth, the central nervous system is notified and the motor sequence of swallowing takes place automatically without any conscious participation.

Prototypes of Human Communication Systems in Animals

OTTO KOEHLER

One primary function of language is communication. Whenever animals of the same species intend to do something together – hunt, mate, care for their young – they have something to communicate to each other, and this they do through instinctive motor patterns, postures, or sounds which are known as 'releasers'. Animals exhibit these behaviour patterns only at the relevant moment. But an action performed by one animal can infectiously spread the corresponding 'mood', i.e. motivation for the behaviour concerned, to other members of the same species.[1] To take a human example – when one pupil yawns, the whole class will soon be yawning. It is as difficult to prove as it is to deny that the higher animals, at least, experience subjective emotions as part of a 'mood', such as fighting fury, flight-readiness linked with fear, desire for pair-formation, hunger and thirst, pleasure in reunions, the urge to play, status-seeking, and so on.

What these releasers are intended to communicate is immediately understood by all members of the same species, however inexperienced. The innate releasing-mechanisms (IRMs) fit the releasers as a key fits a lock. What the senses have already filtered, the releasing-mechanisms filter once again in accordance with the relevant mood; the hungry animal will only search for food, the sexually aroused for a mate, the weary for a resting place. That these lock-and-key mechanisms function together can be shown through experiments in which young animals, brought up in isolation and having no relevant experience, are offered dummies instead of those stimuli which would normally act as releasers. Peters and his students hatched fish eggs of the

[1] In whom the urge might initially be absent, e.g. an animal might begin to eat and thus stimulate others to eat although they do not appear to be hungry. – MN.

82

species *Tilapia mossambica* or *nilotica*, which had been collected from the mouth of the female. These young fish were reared in isolation, away from their mothers, and had no contact with adult members of their own species. If a globe of the right colour and with a diameter slightly less than that of the length of the adult fish was floated gently near them, the inexperienced young fish would accompany the globe, frequently making perpendicular dives towards it and touching it. If the globe had an opening the size of a mouth, they would all swim into it.

Tilapia tholloni do not take their eggs into the mouth but glue them to the ground, where the newly hatched young fasten themselves down by means of adhesive glands on the head. The young of substrate-brooding fish also accompanied the dummy, but did not touch it or seek out its hollow opening.

With *Tilapia macrocephala*, it is the male which takes the eggs into its mouth; but when the larvae are hatched it does not lure them back again and they swim off leaderless in swarms, as do *tholloni*. This latter species lays the greatest number of eggs, but they are the smallest and the poorest in yolk; the small larvae are the fastest in consuming their yolk sac. The eggs of *macrocephala*, on the other hand, are by far the largest. It takes twenty (instead of ten) days for the yolk sac to disappear, and only about twenty eggs are laid.

The two species which have mouth-brooding mothers are roughly intermediate with respect to the characteristics we have mentioned. The young of *tholloni*, the first to swim freely, were also the first to accompany the dummy in Peters' experiments; the young of the two species with mouth-brooding mothers did so at a later stage. The *macrocephala* did not swim with the dummy at all, just as they did not accompany their mouth-brooding father. But when Brestowski drained some of the yolk from their eggs they developed markedly faster, and at their thus artificially advanced 'age' swam after the globe and even sought entrance. Although in their natural life they never do this, they have somehow inherited a capacity which they do not normally use. They 'oversleep' the phase during which they would accompany the parent as long as they are constrained by the yolk.

All these behaviour patterns have been quantitatively studied.

Of the sixteen possible ways of cross-breeding between the four *Tilapa* species, seven proved to be readily fertile. All the above-mentioned differences were inherited in intermediate form, apparently through interaction of several pairs of genes. Here we have experimental evidence that an innate releaser mechanism can be inherited. The assumption is that the mouth-brooders have descended from the substrate-brooders, and this is supported by many clues; it is particularly strongly supported by the fact that the larvae of the three mouth-brooding species show rudimentary, non-functional attachment glands, in exactly the same place as in the substrate-brooders. This type of behaviour, showing a somnambulant sureness in situations which are experienced for the first time, used to be called 'wisdom of the species'. It is based on the innateness of instinctive behaviour patterns, with their accompanying releaser mechanisms. There is an innate capacity for communication in all members of a species, together with comprehension of the significance of the releaser mechanisms. This innate comprehension has nothing to do with intelligence. All innate features are self-evident and have nothing to do with achievement.

Communicative human motor patterns are also innate, for instance shouting, crying, smiling, and laughing in babies. Many people, even child specialists, used not to believe this, insisting that it was the loving mother who taught her child to smile. But even seven-month (premature) babies who have never seen their mothers have smiled in their incubators, first on one side of their faces and then symmetrically, exactly like those born at full term. Even an embryo of no more than four months smiled unilaterally when it was touched on the cheek. Babies born blind also smile in the same way at the same age as normal babies, that is at eight months old; blind babies also move their hands to and fro in play within what would be their field of vision, and like normal children follow the movements of their hands with rolling movements of their blind eyes. They do not roll their eyes mechanically and continuously, but follow the movements of their hands as soon as they can move them, just as if they could see. The attentive observer of a normal child probably thinks that when it does anything at all with its hands the child has started to practise eye-control of manipulation, so that later it will be able to thread needles and handle delicate machinery. But the identical behaviour of a blind child shows that the decisive preconditions for the co-ordination of eye and manipulation movements are entirely innate. The smiling baby gives us pleasure, its well-being communicates itself unequivocally to us. But when the child cries we have to decide what is wrong with it. Can releasers in animals really only communicate 'moods', or can they also communicate individual experience that might be useful to others? In one case at least the answer is yes.

It is inborn in the honey-bee to dance when it comes home from a good source of food. This releaser stimulates the other members of the hive to collect. In addition, the dance tells, first, when the food is available; secondly, how far away it is; thirdly, in which direction from the hive it is; and fourthly, what it consists of. At its first participation in a 'collecting' dance, even a bee which has never yet collected already understands the precise significance of the dance. Even more informative are the dances executed when bees swarm, in which each scout bee demonstrates with its leading dance where it wants to take the swarm. The more favourable it finds the spot it has found, the more insistently it 'praises' it, the livelier and longer will be its dance. In this manner it attracts more and more fellow-dancers, which eventually fly to the spot, inspect the food source and, if it seems to be better than any of the others offered, join this particular 'party'. Voting is truly democratic, and finally the best of all the proposed places is agreed upon. Karl von Frisch has provided us with the information about all this, the most beautiful symbolic language yet discovered in the world of living creatures. He has also described a number of other animal capabilities which humans lack.

Animal languages are innate. Human beings, by contrast, have to learn the words of their mother tongue. Many song-birds have the necessary ear, memory, and skill of vocal mimicry to be able to talk, and so we shall briefly compare their vocal development with that of the human baby.

Sooner or later the baby begins to babble. We are told by linguists and child psychologists that babies eventually form all

85

the vowels, diphthongs, consonants, and sibilants which occur in all the languages on earth, and in addition perform actions such as the common blowing of bubbles with spittle – something which certainly no adult has taught them. The older infant says 'dadadada', that is, practises certain sounds in exhausting repetition while listening to itself. Very early on it composes, with all the single sounds it has learnt to master, a long, constantly changing monologue, in which various tone modulations and cadences of adult speech are imitated with great exactitude. Since infants born deaf babble exactly like normal ones, it can be said of the human child that it possesses the entire sound range belonging to its species, more precisely its phonetic motor patterns, from birth, just like any animal. The difference here between human beings and other animal species lies merely in the extent of their ability to learn. Human beings have to learn most of their word-sounds.

Franz Sauer bred single whitethroats from eggs. Throughout their life they were kept in a sound-proof box and could hear only themselves. Yet as early as the fifth day of their life, they all uttered the same 'tsiep' when they begged for food, on the eleventh day the same 'idat', and later on they had developed a total of twenty-four individual calls, all exactly like those of contemporaries of the same species which had grown up normally in the open. Just like them, Kasper Hauser,[1] in solitary confinement, composed from the sounds he innately commanded his own juvenile songs; the infantile sound-poems he softly chanted may be directly compared to a baby's babbling monologue.

The song-bird hidden in a thicket is totally dedicated to its song, singing 'for art's sake'. It keeps up this 'juvenile' song until the following spring. Thereafter the song is reduced to only a few motifs, used for specific purposes and charged with emo-

[1] Kasper Hauser, the subject of much literature in his own time and later, ncluding Verlaine's poem *Sagesse*, written in 1881, was a foundling who appeared in Nuremberg in 1828. He grew up in the wild state, totally out of contact with any human being, in the manner of the famous wolf-children in India who could not speak or walk upright when they were found. He died in 1833 at an assumed age of about twenty-one. It is thought today that he was autistic. – MN.

tion: an urgent beseeching call uttered immediately before pairing takes place, a war-like fanfare meant to scare away rivals, and a few more. All bird songs and calls are faster, louder and higher in tone when the bird's excitement increases. This also happens in human speech and in music. Sauer's hand, presented to individual caged birds, sometimes represented a territorial rival and sometimes a female mate, and he succeeded in calling forth spring song motifs. These calls also resembled those of each bird's free-living fellows. The whitethroat, with its complex song repertoire for all the different phases of its life, does not need a tutor. But this does not necessarily mean that it cannot learn anything beyond what it already knows; this is something that has not yet been investigated with this particular species.

The process just described takes a different course in different song-bird species. Many begin with an instinctive juvenile song repertoire similar to that of the whitethroat. Chaffinches reared in isolation, which hear only themselves, form a relatively undifferentiated pattern of song, just a little shorter than that of the chaffinch which has grown up in the wild. But if, in early spring, such a bird is allowed to hear the song of the local male chaffinches, then it begins to sing like them, and in this way a dialect emerges. Such a dialect has, for instance, been conserved without alteration in the area around Egge in the Teutoburger Forest for more than twenty years now. Many of the peculiarities of these dialects seem to come about by imitation of short passages from the songs of other bird species. As early as 1740, Baron von Fernau at Rosenau Castle near Coburg had a corner in his forest where the chaffinches sang like tree-pipits: he had put chaffinches less than a year old into an aviary with tree-pipits, and after they had learnt to imitate the pipits' song he settled them in a corner of the forest which was free of chaffinches. Human dialects would seem to come about in the same fashion. The formation of dialects demonstrated in a number of song-bird species is one of the best known examples of animal traditions in the literal sense.

The Californian white-crowned sparrow (*Zonotrichia*) is another dialect singer. When only three to eight weeks old it acquires the exact idiom of the father, though its vocal equipment is not yet up to imitating its parent, even approximately. It can do that only very much later, even without having heard its model since the imprinting took place. If it should become deaf before its vocal instruments have matured for the spring-territory song, then its impeccable memory will not help it, it will never be a dialect singer. If, however, it has had the chance to hear itself imitating what it has heard when young, then it can go on doing it, even if immediately afterwards it becomes deaf – an amazing parallel with the differences between the inability to speak found in children born deaf and the capacity to use language in those who became deaf later.

Imitative birds, like European marsh warblers and icterine warblers, imitate many strange bird voices and incorporate them into their own specific song. Nicolai proved after eight years' work that young whydah birds which, like our cuckoo, grow up in other birds' nests, learn the whole repertoire of their foster-parents and foster-siblings, but only with a particular species of foster-parent. The male whydah bird may only mate with a female if he can imitate convincingly enough, close to the appropriate host nest, the song with which the host male leads the host female to his nest. The entire selection pressure acts on the bird's ability to imitate, in this case helping to produce different species. Tretzel found near Erlangen crested larks which could imitate the whistle of a shepherd to his sheepdog so perfectly that the dog responded when their call was played on a tape. The shepherd's whistle was extremely unmusical, with rhythm, intervals, and pitch varying grotesquely. The imitators composed from the cacophony of the model something like a musical motif, consisting of pure intervals, constant pitch, and strictly kept rhythm. The birds, as it were, invented a theme for the involuntary variations of the shepherd. The neighbouring larks imitated this, and the young imitated their parents. This is a typical example of how family and local dialects originate.

Unsurpassed, with the single exception of the Shama thrush, is the high quality of mimicry achieved by the grey parrot, whose imitations can be confused with the original. Sometimes it learns certain sounds, as well as human words, in relation to particular situations. My bird said 'Hello' when anybody lifted the telephone receiver, because its previous owner had always answered thus, and for the same reason it said 'See you again' if anybody went out of the room. Two other words which it had learned earlier were merged into one made-up word, which was shouted every evening with immense vigour until its cage was covered and the light turned out. In exactly the same way, children comprehend word-sounds and their meaning from the situations in which they hear them, or alternatively they invent words which they use by matching them accurately with the situation. Only with its first phrase, consisting of two or more words and corresponding to actual facts, a phrase formed by its own initiative, does the child surpass the parrot. So far, no imitative bird has composed a meaningful two-word phrase entirely afresh from two separately inherited or acquired sounds.

Of the nineteen preliminary stages so far known to lead to human music and human speech, we have discussed only the following in relation to animals. First, the innate ability to communicate through the medium of instinctive sounds and motor patterns, which not only transmit 'moods' (in the ethological sense already explained) but can also relate to the overall situation, announcing or requesting something. Secondly, the generally comparable specific behavioural motivation and responsiveness of the innate releasing mechanisms, on the basis of which some display patterns can be directly understood even beyond species barriers. Thirdly, the capacity to give an exact vocal rendering of what has been heard. Fourthly, absolute pitch, and related to this the ability to transpose a melody into a different prescribed key. Fifthly, the ability to compose. Sixthly, innate or acquired capacity for action tied to a specific situation, which acts as a preliminary stage for genuine concept-formation. Seventhly, the innately comprehensible real language symbolism of bees.[1] Eighthly, non-verbal thinking, that is the ability to form

[1] Language symbolism, that is, an unequivocal association of symbol – an unmistakable sound, expression or posture – with communicable meaning, may be assumed to operate when, for instance, baboons announce the appearance of a leopard with a 'double bellow' (Altmann) or when, with Japanese short-tailed macaques, the sound 'kaa' produces dispersal in all members of the troop, or 'kuan' (uttered by the alpha-male) produces the reaction of dead silence, hiding, or maximum readiness for flight. But all

images and concepts independently of the use of words, to form judgements which conform with factually consistent behaviour and which, if a word language were later to arise, would form the principal precondition for its existence and effectiveness.

The higher animals are close to human beings in non-verbal thinking, sensory abstraction, ability to expand concepts, transmission, and visual and aural Gestalt perceptions. But evidence is scant, in creatures other than man, of any rudimentary naming of non-verbal images, concepts and judgements, through which we arrived at language and became true human beings. A mated pair of ravens, studied by Gwinner, gives us one example of such rudiments. The male imitated the barking of dogs and the female the gobble of turkeys. When the male escaped on two occasions, the female barked and the male returned. When the female was transferred to another aviary, the male sat permanently in the only corner of the cage from which he could catch a glimpse of her aviary and gobbled like a turkey. Exactly the same behaviour was observed by Kneutgen with a pair of Shama thrushes. The irresistible 'kuducks' of my grey parrot constituted a verbal command of its own invention.

If animals already possess so many roots of language, why do none of them talk as human beings do? The answer is similar to the one which we should give to the question of what was the origin of life, which has remained largely unanswerable despite considerable scientific advances in recent decades. We find abundant individual characteristics comparable to those of life in inanimate matter, but nowhere are they found all together. In the same way, we can recognise all the initial stages and pre-

---

these connections, which have as yet been inadequately examined – warning cries, distress-calls, etc. – can only be understood in the context of a specific situation, with the sole exception of the bee's dance, which exclusively communicates a goal that is not immediately perceptible and the reward which may be anticipated. It comes as something of a surprise in evolutionary thinking to find that, as far as we know at present, this latter faculty is present only in the most social insect, and not in a single vertebrate, not even the apes most closely related to man. It can be fairly said, however, that no higher animal has been nearly so consistently and so extensively investigated as has the bee, thanks to Karl von Frisch and his two generations of students. – O.K.

conditions of human music and language in animals, but most unequally distributed among different animal species, and entirely combined only in one. When our ancestors began to speak, they became human, as every small child does today. It was thanks to the animals which remained animals that man was permitted to become human.

Non-Verbal Thinking

OTTO KOEHLER

According to one ancient legal definition, human life begins with the first cry of the newborn baby. But the biologist knows that both the egg cell and the sperm cell were alive, that the new inhabitant of the earth originated from their union, and equally that each of the intermediate stages was alive. There are good reasons why nobody has so far attempted to explain the 'psychology of the embryo'. It is equally impossible to state at what stage in the development of the human embryo consciousness begins, and to determine just where, in the history of the evolutionary ascent from unicellular organism to man, this consciousness came into being. It is not possible to draw sharp dividing lines in continuous processes, just as nobody can say at what point of the estuary the River Elbe ceases to exist and the Baltic Sea begins.

Life is an uninterrupted process. Of course, death may put an end to an individual life at any moment; but the species lives on. It is quite certain that life must have originated at some point from non-life, just as it is apparent that the process cannot be repeated under the external environmental conditions which exist today. Scientists may have fragmentary concepts, based on experimental research findings, of how individual steps may have taken place, but the primeval generation of life as a whole remains a mystery. All natural scientists are fully conscious of their ignorance in these vital matters – hence their becoming modesty. On the other hand, they are quite confident about what they *do* know. Biologists know that from the moment life existed it was capable of reproducing itself, and that it has never ceased to do so. A single, living cell divides into two and continues to live in both its halves. Even before the cell divided itself, its nucleus divided itself; at that point, or even earlier, each chromosome in the nucleus is split into two equal longitudinal halves. Each of these halves will be stored in one of the two daughter cells, and in this way each daughter cell will possess exactly the same chromosomes as did the mother cell. I say advisedly not *similar* chromosomes, but the *same* ones, in the sense that a person remains the same person at every stage of his existence.

All the chromosomes living today in the cells of every living organism constructed of cells could probably be traced through an uninterrupted series of divisions back to the chromosomes of the first living cells which existed on earth. The plasma of the cells is equally continuous. Since, in the last resort, hereditary transmission consists of processes involving chromosomes and plasma, the laws of heredity are the same for all flora and fauna. The most ancient rocks are considerably more than three thousand million years old. That relatives of even the highest invertebrate phyla living today existed in the Cambrian Age, which began around five hundred and fifty to five hundred and seventy million years ago, has been proved beyond doubt. Traces have been found of the even earlier existence of lower plants, of planktonic polychaete worms, brachiopods, and crustacea. These date back more than one thousand million years, and barely classifiable remains of the lowest plants have been found to date back more than two thousand million years. But even these must have had their ancestors. The beginning of life is as impossible to pin down by a date as is the origin of the earth itself – which in its present form is thought to be four and a half thousand million years old. Three thousand million years is perhaps too modest an estimate for the evolutionary history of life. During this time, more species of animals have died out than the number which continue to exist. These in their turn will have to make room for new species at some time in the future. Ancient fathers of the church spoke of *creatio continua*. The cast-iron laws of nature, according to which the planets circle round the sun, atoms cluster together to become molecules and life continues to exist in the form of individual species, do not solve the mystery of nature; on the contrary, they point to the Glory of the Eternal.

The uniform origin of all life makes it possible to draw comparisons. For instance, we human beings, like all vertebrates, smell with our noses, see with our eyes, hear with our ears. We have teeth and hair as have other mammals, and like them we drink our mother's milk from her breast. Our behaviour shows similarities with that of other mammals at comparable stages. As human beings we share with mammals our chromosomes and our nervous systems. We also share the products of the latter: spatial and temporal orientation, instincts, motivational states and drives, emotions and the innate releaser mechanisms determining which external situation will satisfactorily elicit which instinctive behaviour pattern, without our having to learn the process. Furthermore, we share with other mammals the ability to learn, and finally, the faculty of *non-verbal thinking*, which is what we shall now discuss. From innumerable examples which prove the same points, I have selected just two from work carried out at institutes in Königsberg and Freiburg.

After three months' training, blind mice learned to run almost without error through a labyrinth, which required that they should make the right decisions at about twenty T-junctions. W. Dinger eliminated the Ariadne's thread of urine droplets which each mouse deposited along its path by thoroughly cleaning the aluminium strips composing the runways of the labyrinth. He also nullified any directional effects of sound distribution in the laboratory by rotating the axis of the maze after each run. Each new elimination of unintentional aids at first produced a regression, but this was quickly overcome; quite soon the mice were making hardly any mistakes. Each mouse was then put into four different variations of the same maze in turn, and made scarcely any more mistakes than it had in the original one, in spite of the fact that it had been given *no additional training*. In the first variation, the linear dimensions of the maze were doubled. In the second, the angles were distorted so that the mouse, instead of turning through ninety degrees each time, had to turn alternately through forty-five degrees and one hundred and thirty-five degrees. In the third variation, the sequence of the second was reversed, and the mouse had to turn alternately through one hundred and thirty-five degrees and forty-five degrees. Finally the training maze was reconstructed as a mirror image.

The success of the mouse's *transformations* (i.e. where it immediately understood a new situation without additional learning) proved that the animal had a *figurative image* of the right direction in the training maze and could transpose this image meaningfully to fit the shape of the new labyrinth. It could make figurative abstractions of the length of the runs and the width of the angles. On top of that, it at once understood when the maze had been transformed into its mirror image, and was able to transpose its own concept of the path to be taken. In the sense given by Wolfgang Köhler, this is true *Gestalt* perception: the mouse had a figurative *conception* of shape, which it could transpose equally well into dimensions, angles, and direction of rotation, as we read and write the letters of the alphabet, recognising them regardless of their size, or whether they are vertical or slanting, leaning towards the left or the right, or even written as mirror images. If we human beings memorise a route, through a series of landmarks, we can also find our way back simply by changing right to left as in mirror images, and by reading the series of landmarks backwards. Many animals can do this at least as well as human beings. The mouse *makes a decision* at each junction: one way is correct, the other incorrect. Such calculations, employing images, concepts, and decisions with a perceptual basis, do not carry any name because no verbal language exists for them; we refer to them as 'non-verbal thinking'. Only human beings have given names to their elements, since only human beings can speak. But if we know what we want to say, it is because we have thought it out beforehand at least partially in a non-verbal manner. Such human non-verbal thinking can be equated to that found at comparable levels in the higher animals.

Our second example is concerned with non-verbal counting by animals. Pigeons were taught to discriminate between groups of four and five grains of corn, when both groups lay next to each other; it was proved that they can 'see numbers'. Furthermore, they learned to pick up only five grains from a heap of corn, i.e. to *operate* with the number 'five'. It has been proved in many experiments that both these talents have an upper limit which is constant in a species, though variable from one species to another: five for pigeons, six for budgerigars and jackdaws, seven for ravens, Amazon and grey parrots, magpies, and squirrels. As far as we know from parallel experiments with human beings, man does exactly as well or as badly as animals in non-verbal counting, that is if he is prevented from using the names which signify numbers for him.

The above-mentioned animals and birds also succeeded in carrying out very demanding tasks without new conditioning. Four species of birds and squirrels learned to make the so-called 'choice from sample'. Five dishes had lids with tacks on them arranged like the spots on dominoes: three, four, five, six, and seven. In front of them on the floor was the 'sample', a lid with (for instance) five tacks on it. In this case, the raven which had learned its task would open only the dish with five tacks on its lid. When the number of tacks on the model was changed (preserving the 'domino' pattern), the bird would invariably open the dish which had the same number of tacks on its lid as the model. But we abruptly stopped arranging the tacks like the spots on dominoes, and put them each time in completely random order, taking particular care that the pattern of the tacks on the sample lid was completely different from that on the lid with the same number of tacks which the bird was expected to open.

My raven from Königsberg at once got the hang of it. With no new conditioning he performed almost better than before. The same happened when, in a third test, conditions were made even more difficult, and instead of tacks, spots of plasticine of constantly changing forms, sizes, and positions yielded an almost astronomically high number of different possibilities. Only at this stage, after the elimination of all irrelevantly helpful clues, was it possible to say that the bird chose solely by *the number which it had seen before*, the only number out of five which corresponded to that of the sample.

A reverse experiment was equally successful. It involved picking out one lid which had a different number of tacks when all the others bore the same number. A squirrel belonging to Dr

Hassmann learned to choose the lid with three tacks when it was offered five dishes with lids bearing four, four, four, three, and four. When the animal was offered three, three, three, four, and three, it chose the four, and so on, through all forty-two combinations which can be made from the numbers nought to six. In each of these tests, the only lid which deviated from the other four bearing identical numbers was put alternately in five different places. Accordingly, forty-two multiplied by five (i.e. two hundred and ten) possibilities followed one another in a predetermined random order. Even many human beings might have taken some time to learn this principle of choice, if confronted with the experiments without verbal explanation, as with the squirrel.

The two abilities described, of *seeing* and *operating with* numbers, have no common figurative basis. We can readily connect them with each other because of our possession of names for numbers. If I tell a child that it may eat as many cherries as the number of times I lift my finger, it will *add up to the numbers which it has seen*, i.e. it will operate with numbers. If, on the other hand, I ask the child how many cherries it has eaten and it replies by lifting its finger, then I see operated numbers. The only thing which connects these two abilities is the named number. Since animals, which cannot speak, lack names, it might have been expected that an animal, unlike a child which can talk, would be incapable of at the same time operating with numbers it had seen and perceiving the operated numbers. Yet it has been proved that animals can learn to make the two connections separately. A jackdaw learned to operate with numbers it had seen, always picking up only two meal-worms out of a circle of many after seeing two dots in the middle of the circle, and four after seeing four dots. Even better results have been achieved with parrots. A magpie belonging to Dr Sauters dealt with visually perceived numbers the other way round. If it found, after uncovering a long row of covered dishes, three titbits in all, it would afterwards open out of four dishes with one, three, five, and seven dots on their lids, only the one with three dots on the lid; and only the one with seven dots after it had found seven titbits in all in the row. An Amazon parrot belonging to Dr H.

Braun performed correctly when quintuple choices were offered, and her grey parrot ('Jakob') could deal with numbers which he had only *heard*. If he heard, for instance, two sounds from a recorder, a metronome or any other source as he walked up to a row of dishes, he would continue to lift lids until he found two titbits, and then leave the rest untouched. After a signal of three sounds he would look for three, after four for four titbits, and so on. In other words, he continued to open lids, no matter how many, until he found the number indicated by the sound signal. The signals were extensively varied in duration, pitch, tone-colour, and intervals between them, and any human being would have been hard put to keep up with the grey parrot.

This same Jakob later dealt with a series of dishes involving all the above-mentioned combinations up to the number eight. After he had learned from Dr Braun to follow sounds instead of dots, and then been allowed to forget this exercise altogether, he learned from P. Lögler to observe and count light flashes, so that, for instance, after six totally arhythmical flashes of light in succession, he started to open the lids of dishes until he had found six titbits, and after seven flashes continued to search until he had found the seventh titbit. After this, Jakob was able to switch over at once from the arhythmical light flashes to equally arhythmical notes played on the recorder, and then back again without any further training. The bird thus understood the similarities of numbers in x light signals and x sound signals; he had achieved a so-called 'heteromodal transposition'. It is probable that this same feat had previously been achieved only by Mrs Nadie Koht's chimpanzee, which invariably picked out from a heap of variously shaped stones the one the shape of which Mrs Koht had just shown it in the flat of her hand. When she then put its hand into a sack, it would pick out the shape which matched the model, this time using touch instead of sight to find the form it had just seen.

Apart from these feats, Jakob achieved a further fourteen series of tasks, for which he had in no way been trained. Of these, we shall describe only one. Jakob had learned, after hearing two sound signals, to lift the unmarked lids of dishes until he found two titbits, and after only one sound signal to look for only one titbit. Lögler now offered him a choice of lids marked with one or two dots; after hearing two sounds Jakob lifted the lid with two dots, and after one sound the lid with one dot. Thus, he made the spontaneous transition from a 'simultaneous–successive' association to a 'simultaneous–simultaneous' association.

The reverse transition from simultaneous to successive associations was achieved twenty-one years earlier by a pigeon which learned to pick up two grains lying close together on the narrow end of a strip of cardboard, but to ignore the single grain which lay at the opposite end. When the inner grain of the group of two was slowly pushed towards the middle of the strip, the pigeon still chose the group of two, in spite of the growing distance between the two grains. Only when the inner grain was exactly in the middle of the strip, equidistant from both the other grains, did the pigeon as often pick either the pair on the left, or the pair on the right, or even the two outside ones. It then ate two and left one – responding to the number two. The bird had changed from the *simultaneous* seeing of numbers to the *successive* dealing with numbers.

These two spontaneous, unlearned progressions from one basic capacity to another would seem particularly significant in forming one strut, as it were, in the bridge between the two possibilities of using numbers exemplified in simultaneous and successive presentations of objects, a bridge which cannot be formed by visual perception alone.

Thorough examination of all the other counting experiments dating back half a century teaches the same lesson. So far as we know, adult human beings are in no way superior to animals in non-verbal thinking, where matters that actually concern animals are involved. Sometimes, in pathfinding for instance, man is far inferior. The human infant thinks exactly like an animal, in a purely non-verbal fashion: it knows the bottle and the teddy bear long before it has learnt to call them 'bottle' and 'teddy bear'. Once it has learned the words, it will fetch these things when a verbal command is given, though only much later, when it can itself say 'bottle' and 'teddy', will it be able to ask for them. Dogs, elephants, and dolphins can be taught to obey verbal commands. A talented grey parrot can speak up to one hundred words. But, as has been said already, no animal has ever spontaneously formed a new meaningful phrase out of two words which have been learnt separately. A small child can manage this once it is able to speak only a very few words. With the first two-word phrase expressing a response to objective reality, its superiority over every animal is finally and unequivocally manifested.

Animals cannot name, but they possess the power of non-verbal thinking. Such thinking fits the uses to which it is put in the same way as any organ is fitted to its use, and for the same reasons. Only man, when he begins to speak in his earliest childhood, as his ancestors did earlier in the history of his evolution, gives names to the elements of non-verbal thinking which he shares with animals. Human language is thus suitable for the description and reporting of everything, both in our external environment and in our internal imaginative world, just as non-verbal thinking by animals suits their particular needs. At the same time, man is lifted far above any animal by reason of the language he possesses, which animals do not, and because there is a perpetual dynamic interplay in his consciousness between verbal and non-verbal thinking, an incessant give-and-take by both, during which a single new word can widen the framework with explosive force. Consciousness of himself, power over his own drives, a sense of responsibility and duty, freedom of will, morality, religion, art, and science are the privileges of the articulate creature alone. But always and everywhere, non-verbal thinking is also present in man, so that the deepest and most profound strata of his being can always respond. The human heart often offers better counsel than human words, because words match their use only insofar as they are un-equivocal and appropriate.

Anyone who opens his mouth knows beforehand what he wants to say – not as a sermon learned by heart, but at least at the non-verbal level. He will say the same thing in very different ways, according to the person to whom he speaks, and having said it he will be aware that his words were never completely fitting, never fully explanatory, that the best has remained un-said, for words are really only like a veil masking the non-verbal image which stands before our inner eye, never the image itself. And even the image itself is far from being reality.

Notwithstanding all the precious gifts we owe to language, all the things which make us human, we should not forget our ancient power of non-verbal thinking, which we owe to and share with the animals, which ties our thinking to the earth on which we have our being, and which is, in all earthly matters, the touchstone by which the word proves its worth.

Chance, Necessity, and Plan in the Living Universe

OTTO KOEHLER

No one has defined what life is. Words cannot match the infinite complexities of the wealth of natural events. But we can enumerate the essential characteristics of life. Life is a matter of *individual entities* at various stages of organisation: viruses, bacteria, unicellular and multicellular creatures, animals. It transforms matter, energy, form; it develops, grows, procreates, inherits, possesses responsiveness which can culminate in an inner life. Carl Ernst von Baer, the great master of biology, singled out the urge towards a goal as a specially significant mark of life.

Comparable qualities exist in inanimate matter. Water and fire also exhibit transformations characteristic of matter and energy, crystals grow, the cosmos is organised in all its dimensions: the movements of the planets are predictable down to the smallest detail; the movements and internal oscillations of atoms are subject to statistical laws. But never do all these characteristics come together simultaneously in inanimate matter; the boundary is thus clearly discernible between animate and inanimate matter. Von Baer has said that purpose is a task set by human will, presupposing free choice; a goal, by contrast, is a prescribed achievement, which can also be arrived at through necessity. The fruit machine spews out coins, the hen produces her daily egg; since these actions happen continuously, necessity must lie behind them. 'It is the true task of natural science to comprehend the manner in which natural life consists of goal-oriented necessities, and of goals necessarily pursued. The purpose of individual life would appear to be to live, procreate and preserve the species.' 'Nature cannot further her goals in any other way than through the effectiveness of natural laws. Without these, any effectiveness and any pursuit of a goal would be sheer magic.' 'Harmony is composed of goals and the natural laws which will bring them about. The ability to pursue purposes and goals, and to choose the most effective means of doing so, is what we call *reason*. The whole of nature *operates* in accordance with reason; or if we think of effective performance as the fundamental principle that binds nature together, all nature *is* in accordance with reason.' These words of von Baer represent a true synthesis of Plato and Democritus.

Anyone who observes plants and animals and compares them with one another will see similarities and differences. No human being, no animal, no leaf is an exact replica of any other; at the same time we can easily distinguish the leaf of the lime tree from that of the chestnut tree. Men, apes, and kangaroos, with their hair, mother's milk, and so on, correspond to the *structural* and *functional plan* of the mammals, which together with that of the birds, reptiles, amphibians, and fish, is subject to the vertebrate plan. *Amphioxus*, the so-called lancet fish, is not a vertebrate, but its design is the theme upon which all vertebrates base their variations. Its skeletal chord consists only of the notochord throughout its entire existence. Every vertebrate which develops from an egg goes through the initial stage of possessing a notochord, and afterwards forms from the notochord a cartilaginous vertebral column which in the shark remains unchanged during its lifetime. Among all higher vertebrates bone, during a third stage of development, replaces most of the cartilage; with man part of this process takes place only after birth.

No one would put up a tent, burn it down, replace it by a wooden building, pull this down, and finally build in stone the cathedral that was meant to stand on the site in the first place. But in the history of evolution such roundabout methods are common. Every multicellular animal begins its development as a unicellular egg, like the protozoa. In the subsequent segmentation it may be compared to a colony of protozoa; at the stage of the blastula it resembles a *Volvox*, and when it becomes a two-layered gastrula it resembles a coelenterate like the *Hydra*. In this way every creature including man, in the course of its own growth, passes through developmental stages at which the lower species have remained static. Much is developed which is no longer of use, such as the gill slits and the jaw hinge of the bony fish, which are present in the human embryo before the human jaw hinge is formed. In a highly improbable change of function in evolutionary history, the ciliated grooves of the gill basket became the human thyroid gland, and the more ancient of the two jaw hinges the human auditory ossicles. The young Goethe wrote: 'Nature is always creating new forms; what exists now never existed before; what existed in the past does not return; everything is new, and yet it is ever the same.' This is in fact a sober statement of the metamorphosis of form which we have already mentioned: with strictest regularity the eggs of chickens will always become chickens, the eggs of tree frogs, tree frogs. Such everyday events, like the starry sky, inspire the human on-looker with awe; it is the laws, the regularity of all natural processes that constitute the mystery which moves us to explore all that can be comprehended and to venerate in silence what cannot be explored.

The fact that all life develops only from its own kind, in the same way as the previous generation, we call *heredity*. Just as Copernicus, Kepler, and Newton analysed the harmony of the spheres, so has the science of genetics analysed hereditary trans-mission with such precision that prophecies about future generations come true with extraordinary regularity. All the body cells of a human being contain the same forty-six chromosomes, twenty-three of these coming from the egg cell of the mother, twenty-three from the sperm cell of the father. Before a cell splits, all forty-six chromosomes must split lengthwise into two equal halves, of which one will end up in the one daughter nucleus and the other in the second one. Both new nuclei there-fore have the same chromosomes as their mother nucleus, and all body-cell nuclei of a human being have the same chromosomes as the original egg cell.[1] The chromosomes contain the hereditary factors, which Mendel discovered, and distribute them during the formation of the germ cells and the fertilisation process resulting in the next generation. The laws of heredity are ful-filled in exactly the way in which Mendel established them in his

[1] But the germ (sex) cells contain only half as many chromosomes as the body cells, one of each pair, either the paternal or the maternal one.

day, without knowing anything about chromosomes. Hereditary processes take place in the cells of all cellular creatures, from the unicellular algae to the oak tree and man, and are fundamentally the same throughout. Since no chromosome is generated except by longitudinal division of one of its own kind, all chromosomes and all nuclei, as well as all plasma of all creatures living today, go back in a direct, unbroken series of division sequences to the chromosomes, the nuclei, and the plasma of the first cells, which originated on earth something like three thousand million years ago. This fact alone proves the indispensability to the whole field of biology of the theory of the origin of species – which is still, to be sure, a theory; but one as firmly established as the atomic theory, which few laymen would venture to question. All the component fields of biology support the theory of evolution and are supported by it. How can anybody claim that it has been disproved because it does not, in itself, explain everything? Natural science is based on facts. There are an infinite number of them, while human research and knowledge are limited. We confess in all humility that we know practically nothing in comparison with the vast quantity of facts there are still to know; but we are certain of the things we do know. We may constantly proclaim knowledge in new words, but the new formula does not make the old one false. It covers both old and new. Yesterday's knowledge is not today's error, but an integral part of the broader law which has since been discovered.

But if all my cells contain the same hereditary matter, why do they look so different from one another as for example those in the liver, the intestines, the hair, the bones, the retina, the brain? And why do they perform such different tasks as digesting, heating, supporting, seeing, and thinking? A biological character is never essentially hereditary; only its individual variation is hereditary. External circumstances, which vary locally, influence nuclei of identical heredity and determine which of all possible hereditary characters will result here, which there. The physiology of genetics teaches us to recognise such external factors. Hans Spemann took from the embryo of an orange speckled toad a fragment destined to become part of the skin of the stomach, and transplanted it into that part of an equally young salamander embryo which was to be its mouth. There resulted a salamander larva with the mouth of a tadpole. The embryo fragment obeyed the dictates of the foreign locality; thus it became mouth instead of stomach skin. But, irrespective of which part of the body it formed, it remained toad-matter, forming the cells of a toad. The developing organism in all its parts is astonishingly adaptable to external circumstances.

It is through external factors determining evolution that we have acquired knowledge of such things as differences in plasma, neurological and neuro-secretory processes, and hormones which penetrate through the wall of a cell into the neighbouring cell or circulate within the blood; we already know the chemical composition of some of these hormones. So although we know certain disconnected things about cells, we still know very little about, for instance, how and why, in the incomprehensibly complicated process of cell growth, each cell takes its cue at the right time and in the right place, so that in spite of inferior hereditary quality, and such handicaps as constriction of the egg cell or transplantation of large parts of the embryo, development will still take place in accordance with the characters and nature of the species. Anyone who claims that any one unifying factor, say entelechy, is the clue to the enigma is no natural scientist, or he has forgotten that he ever was one. The natural scientist has learned to wait, and knows that when he is confronted with a mystery, giving it a name does little to solve it. Nobody has learned how to become rich from the statement that poverty is a result of need.

At the bottom of all fine phrases pointing to unifying factors lies the concept of the planner or architect who organises homogeneous material and employs ignorant workmen, each of whom is given distinct orders. But nobody has ever met this architect. Let us take one example. On the dung of grazing animals grow the fungus-like fruiting bodies of a living creature called *Dictyostelium*, which zoologists classify among the uni-cellular Rhizopoda. But the fruit-body, the sporophore, consists of a hard *multicellular* stem with a drop of water at the top, which is full of tiny spores. In the laboratory, an amoeba will creep out from each spore on to a plate of agar which has been inoculated with bacteria; the amoebae swarm about all over the place, eat and procreate. Suddenly, the confusion ceases. The amoebae creep together to form columns facing in one direction; the rear-guard then presses to the front and forms a tightly packed wedge at the head of each column, the amoebae now standing rigid one above the other about the axis of the column to form stem cells. Other amoebae crawl up the outside of each stem until they reach the top, then becoming spores. So here we have thousands of single-cell organisms suddenly combining in a well co-ordin-ated manner in accord with the structural plan of the species, forming the multicellular sporophore. It has been proved to be a matter of pure chance where, on the agar plate in the laboratory, the centres of activity will form, at what point the columns will unite, which amoeba will end up in which fruit-body, which one will become stem and which end up as a spore. It is impossible to assume a single master-builder; rather, each of the thousands of cells carries within itself the whole of the species' system of responses, obeys and commands at the same time; each and every cell is simultaneously master builder and universal work-man. Virtually the same principle applies to the genetic history of every multicellular structure.

Everywhere in physiology we meet the same contradiction. We always find only single chains of causation. But when we come to describe, compare, and classify morphologically, we see patterns. If the same pattern is constantly reproduced, there must be causation. How could chance always produce identical results? Yet all conclusions about the one final co-ordinating master-builder are wrong. The scientist who researches into causality should not be blamed for understanding only isolated data and never a total process; he should be provided with assistance instead. It has been said that biology merely consists of the study of patterns, and that study of causality is drudgery. For example, I know the design of my motor-car, a harmonious, self-contained construction which enables me to move forward in any direction I choose. During the journey, the engine stalls. Knowledge of my car's design pattern and the destination of my journey will not help at all, but a needle will, with which, after a routine causal investigation, I clear the blocked jet which made the engine stall. The car now takes me to my destination. In exactly the same way an operation at the right time will cure appendicitis, where an understanding of the whole man in good health will be useless.

It has been stated that Mendel's laws of heredity operate through causal processes enacted by chromosomes. But these laws are of a statistical nature. We are not able to predict whether a particular flower of a plant belonging to a second generation of cross-breeding will be red, pink, or white, though we can safely predict that among a hundred of its relatives there will be, roughly, twenty-five red, fifty pink, and twenty-five white flowers. The more numerous the descendants the more precise will be the proportion of one: two: one. The same thing will happen if we toss two different coins. If only we throw them often enough we shall obtain the same proportion of two heads or two tails or one head and one tail.

We can interpret chance as necessity, which we cannot interpret in the case of a single incident either because there are too many factors present that have little or nothing to do with one another, or because we might not be able to examine the situation closely enough, or simply because it is not worth the bother. If a roof tile falls on someone's head, some definite process must have caused the tile to fall, and the victim to be on the spot at the crucial moment. Such a coincidence of causal chains is called an unpredictable necessity by the determinist, chance by the statistician; others would call it bad luck, a cruel fate, a just punishment – or, if the person escaped by a hair's breadth, good luck, manifestation of a kind providence: what actually happened remains the same.

A small island is inhabited by wild rabbits. Perhaps a ship was once wrecked there. If all the crew drowned, rabbits were in luck; not so if just one Robinson Crusoe landed, particularly if his powder remained dry. All matters of population are influenced by historical circumstances, in which the natural scientist sees chance to be much in evidence. The fewer the rabbits that originally landed on the island, the fewer will be the mutated genes which can be inherited by their descendants; this is why so many special island races exist. Mutation, heredity, a high degree of selection, and geographical isolation bring about new races, even demonstrably leading to new species.

We now know that mutations are always undirected. *Direct* adaptation, which makes individual development so goal-oriented, does not exist phylogenetically; it only occurs as the effect of selection upon a hereditary framework broadened by mutation and recombination of genes. Only an organism possessing hereditary factors which permit development in accordance with environmental demands, only an organism which has made timely provision, can survive. We call this '*pre*-adaptation'. Anyone able to swim well could have managed without Noah's Ark. Anyone inclined to deny the part played by chance in evolutionary history and to emphasize its overall regular plan would have to be able to predict just how the present system of plants and animals is going to look in a million years time. If we imagine, furthermore, that when the first cell on earth split into two, one daughter cell had landed on each of two halves of the earth, and that since then two earths, under identical conditions, had been circling around the sun – even then we should not expect to find on the other earth our *Dictyostelium* amoebae, our fire salamanders, our Newfoundland dogs, and civilised man.

Darwin is often reproached for attributing too much to chance. If one were to put all the parts of a watch into a box, such critics claim, one could never shake it so that the watch would re-assemble. This is undeniable. Even if two small wheels happened to come correctly together, the next shaking would make them fall apart again. But the analogy does not hold. Watches cannot mate, divide themselves, or have offspring. No one knows how the first cell originated on earth. But once it appeared, it started to procreate. However random the mutations that occurred, direct adaptation always made the best of them in individual development. What was a disadvantage in one case could be an advantage elsewhere. However small any advantage might have been, slowly but surely it permitted its owner to overtake other individuals which were very slightly inferior. In natural selection, every value is hereditarily consolidated in accordance with strictly regular laws, every possibility is used when its hour comes.

The miracle of eyes with lenses capable of perceiving images – imitated in the camera – occurred in seven quite independent lines of evolution. Mosaic eyes developed independently in five different groups of animals. Similar successive stages of visual performance were repeated in evolutionary history, each by different structural means. The cuttlefish did not take its eye from the predatory bristle worm *Alciopa*, the best image-receiver of its class; nor did the first vertebrates take the cuttlefish's patent. Each discovered its eye for itself. Twelve separate paths led to the ability to see.

Evolutionary structural and functional 'plans' are developed in a peculiar interaction of particular causal necessities and statistically regular chance incidents on the one hand with necessity on the other.

As a result of the common confusion of goal and purpose, some have postulated the obligatory presence of inherent co-ordinators to explain the harmonious interaction of individual organs. In ancient Rome the tribune of the people appeased the rebellious proletarians by telling them his parable of the industrious limbs which refused to feed the lazy stomach; when they let the stomach starve, they themselves disappeared. The nervous system and the hormones are the prime agents passing between all the individual organs, and they work closely together. Where is the site of the body's command centre which man has sought for so long? The ancients located it in the diaphragm, today we locate it somewhere in the brain. But the freshwater polyp has no brain, the sponge does not even have nerve cells, and still their organs co-operate. Man cannot function without a brain, however. In the ascending animal hierarchy, new organs always appear to perform the same old tasks. If, for instance, a stroke destroys part of the brain, then definite capacities will certainly be missing. But nobody has yet found the exact locality of the leading principle in the brain. On the contrary, Erich von Holst has compared the collaboration of all the dependent centres of the nervous system with an ideal parliament, in which nothing is postponed, but everything discussed and put instantly into practice, government and executive being one and the same. The severed tentacle of an octopus pursues prey like an independent creature and carries it when captured to where the mouth previously was. J. von Uexküll was quite right in calling starfish and sea urchins 'reflex republics'.

An observer from another planet, if he were a vitalist (i.e. believed life processes to be not entirely explicable by scientific principles), observing human activity on earth, would postulate the presence of a leader who imprisoned us all in the evenings, released us into the streets during the day and assembled us in certain places at certain hours. He would hardly conceive that each one of us egoists would want to appease his own hunger independently of anyone else, to see only for himself in the cinema, and to read undisturbed in the train. The pattern of distribution seen by the non-human observer would be 'unintentional order', a common phenomenon in nature which we have already noted with the sovereign *Dictyostelium* amoebae, and which we shall now examine in action in an insect community.

The term 'termite madness' is apt in one respect only: all female workers of a colony of any bee-like creatures are siblings with approximately equal faculties. The queen does not reign, but only lays eggs. There is no leader in the hive, no policeman or judge, no threat of prison to force slackers to perform their arduous tasks. No bee 'desires' or is capable of anything other than acting at all times purely for the welfare of the hive. The bee's stomach has two compartments. The front compartment is a repository which cannot digest; the food-gathering bee fills it with nectar and flies home. If the activity of flying causes the sugar content of the insect's blood to sink below the critical level, a muscle opens the exit of the front stomach and permits a little food to percolate into the posterior, 'private' stomach, which can digest it. In this way the bee neither starves nor feasts. Conveyance to the hive of as much nectar as possible is ensured through the reflex of the closing muscle, and its control system is involuntary. To take another example. A swarm of bees settles somewhere, scouts fly out, and each searches until it finds a place suitable for the whole swarm to live. The scouts return and perform the tail-wagging dance before the rest of the swarm.

These dances tell the other bees in what direction and at what distance they can find the recommended places. At first, each dancer tells of a different place, but after a while more and more bees agree on one spot, and once all are agreed the whole swarm flies there. Men only talk of democracy, bees actually carry it out. Everything that these born altruists take for granted would present a tricky problem for man with his free will; hereditary factors and education, particularly in social matters, make man totally different from the bee. No institution – nursery, church, state, law – no customs or manners come anywhere near achieving what these insects are instinctively able to do to perfection. The more tightly packed man's ever-multiplying communities become, the more his social problems press upon him, the more he would do well to learn from animals, instead of looking down on them and disparaging them.

So once again we find ourselves contemplating a pattern of action which some will misinterpret as the result of rational, conscious planning, some principle active within all living creatures, particularly human children and animals. 'The thing most apt to drive a parent wild is a child behaving as a child.' A mother fails to respond to her child in the street, and it tugs in vain at her hand crying: 'Look! Do look!' A person who drives his car over a chicken thinks: 'The silly bird should have known it couldn't cross the road in time!' A fisherman pulling a porpoise into his boat instead of a shoal of fish finds it has torn his net; he lashes out at the porpoise and then throws it back into the water, saying: 'Now you'll remember not to do that again!' Sweatbox pigs, food factory calves and battery hens are bred to become sausages, veal steaks, and egg machines; they must do nothing but eat and are given no room for any other activity.

Comparative behavioural research is vitally necessary, and its results should be made known to ordinary people so that they may learn what animals really need and how to help them. Man should study all other creatures so that he may discover what they lack, study how they express themselves, each and every one of them, every kind of animal, every human people, how a child expresses itself differently even from month to month. And if anyone, instead of carrying out such research, comes out with the 999th answer to the question of what it is that distinguishes man from animal, then we should ask: What animal? Amoeba, bottlenosed whale, or chimpanzee?

It is quite incorrect to say that animals live by instinct and human beings by intelligence. The human baby arrives in the world like a kitten, a creature entirely ruled by instinct. His mind develops gradually at first, as does that of the higher animals, before he is able to speak. With the learning of his mother tongue the infant matures in a different way and then, one hopes, continues to develop in yet another way throughout the rest of his active life. If it were not innate in him to breathe, cough, and sneeze, if he were not born equipped with the ability to suck, swallow, and digest, he would have suffocated or starved to death long before he had time to learn all these actions. As soon as the feathers of the young swift are fully grown, it throws itself out of the nest into the air, avoids every telegraph wire, and returns safe and sound. If birds had to learn how to fly from scratch, every one of them would land on the ground, shattered at the first attempt. Those species-specific motor patterns which cannot be performed straight after birth are not learned. The organism has to wait until the necessary structures are fully developed; then the entire capacity abruptly becomes available and learning can be added only by applying it. The sexual behaviour of the species is inborn, although it will be practised only much later when the genital glands have matured and when other glands have also secreted their chemical messages into the blood in the right proportions.

All instincts are thus inborn. But they become active only when the right appetitive state or 'mood' has come about, evidenced in courtship display for breeding, eating when hungry, drinking when thirsty, tiredness for sleep, fury for fighting, fear for flight, etc. The physiology of the different moods is the same for all vertebrates, including man. In man moods come to a climax subjectively, through the emotions which accompany the course of instinctive behaviour patterns. We suspect that it is the same with animals.

'Look how gaily the fish jump about in the water,' said Tschuang Tse. 'That is the joy of the fish.'

Hui Tse said: 'You are not a fish. How can you know about the joy of the fish?'

Tschuang Tse said: 'I know the joy of the fish from the joy which I experience when I watch them from the bridge.'

Let us try to understand these words, which were spoken more than two thousand one hundred years ago, in the context of evolutionary history, and let us take them literally: as the plasma of animals is the same as our human plasma, their chromosomes the same as our chromosomes, so is their joy similar to our joy, their sorrow, fear, fury, disgust, and pain like ours. By running their emotionally charged course with reference to a suitable object, instinctive behaviour patterns consume the corresponding motivation. The hungry person stills his need by eating, tired creatures sleep their fill; in this way they are liberated for new motivational states ('moods'). Moods and their patterns of changes, the so-called hierarchy of motivational states, are the instinctive part of that complex reality which is commonly called 'will'.

The innate releaser mechanisms determine the object towards which any given instinctive behaviour pattern is directed. The very first time that the mother's breast is offered, the newborn baby sucks. If a substitute is too cold or unpalatable, the baby will refuse it and howl. A hand-reared male rat, as soon as it was sexually mature, was presented with a female rat on heat as the first sight of its own species, and its behaviour was hardly different from that of any experienced male rat. But it was totally uninterested in females of any other species. They lacked the sign stimulus which fitted the hand-reared rat's innate releaser mechanism as a key fits a lock. Throughout its lifetime, an animal searches for the sign stimuli which match the innate releaser mechanisms for the instinct appropriate to its prevailing mood, seeking until it finds them. Then the lock springs open, the instinctive behaviour pattern and its emotion take their course, the motivational state is satisfied and dies away. But if the search, the so-called 'appetitive behaviour', remains unsuccessful for a long period of time, then a drive can become dammed up to the point where excitation breaks through, and the instinctive behaviour pattern takes place in a vacuum or becomes redirected towards a substitute object, as in sucking one's thumb or chewing gum.

New behavioural components may be acquired to join the inherited components of behaviour, innate locomotive activities, orientation mechanisms, instincts, motivational states, emotions, and releaser mechanisms. In a way similar to that in which identical hereditary cells in the growing embryo respond to different external stimuli by developing differing organs and tissues, so learning and experience can modify inherited behaviour in the course of a lifetime. At least from the earthworm upwards, no creature acts purely by instinct; all creatures learn at the same time as they act by instinct, i.e. they build new restrictions into their releaser mechanisms and add new sign stimuli to those they inherited. In this way, the young chick learns to give up pecking at stones and its own claws and to swallow only what tastes good. The innate releaser mechanisms of courtship demand a spouse of the same species. Once a male has found a mate and gets to know her personally, he wants only *his* mate, *his* territory, and so on. What is innate is the measure of *how much* a creature can learn, innate releasing mechanisms determine *what* it can learn, and motivational states determine *when* it finds it easiest to learn and to retain what it has learned. In the case of human beings, who have come to exhibit wide hereditary differences through self-domestication, we talk in a similar way of individual endowment.

In my previous essay in this book I discussed how, in contrast to all other animals, man came to develop a word language and how, through this means, he became man in the true sense. It has been demonstrated that higher animals, along with human children before they can talk, operate with visual, non-verbal concepts, images and judgements, just as an adult man does with words. Instead of trying out a variety of possible courses at random until hitting on the correct solution by accident and then sticking to it, which would be an intelligent procedure, higher animals and human children first think out an approach and then act on the basis of insight. They can remember paths which they have trodden only once before, they can join together for collective action: in short, their capacity for non-verbal thinking allows them to adapt their behaviour directly to new external conditions far more effectively than mere learning would have done. Non-verbal thinking, as we have seen, serves its purpose just as every organ fits its functions, and for the same evolutionary reasons.

Adult man alone has given *names* to all such averbal concepts, ideas, and judgements. In this way, human beings can talk and think in words about things where animals can only think in a non-verbal manner. But often we ourselves think in non-verbal terms just like the higher animals, before we formulate our thoughts into words. And if our non-verbal thinking, which we inherited from the animals, did not serve its function, then our language would also be useless.

But a word is not what it signifies; it is only its symbol, and even then only one-sidedly and ambiguously. Our senses comprehend only a small amount of what goes on around us, purely physically and chemically, and of that small amount the innate releasing mechanisms eliminate everything that does not concern them. Finally, a name can never fully describe what is named, but only what the name-giver comprehends of it. Everybody can cull a different meaning from the same object. In this way, the senses represent a first filter, releasing mechanisms a second, and words a third filter between our experience and the events taking place in our environment. It is for this reason that people sometimes talk past each other and discuss in a vacuum. That is the disadvantage of language. Its immeasurable gain is that it lays the foundations for the stage of free intellectual play which is uniquely reserved for mankind – always, however, in harmony with non-verbal thinking and in constant interchange with it. Now we can dominate our instincts, silencing them instead of blindly following their dictates like animals. Now we can believe in a Higher Being, can be responsible to it and to ourselves, can pursue art and finally science, which opens up a vista of the universe and its history and also of our race, and so permits us to provide, by means of careful planning, for ourselves and our descendants.

It is nearly three thousand years since Plato and Democritus discussed philosophy and science, discoursing sometimes about the whole and sometimes about its parts, about design, chance, freedom and predetermination, vitalism and mechanism, all-embracing faith which is higher than reason, science which belongs only to the physical world and concerns its finite parts only, but has its ever-reproducible, firmly based reliability, its steady tendency to progress. But arguments about words still rage, sometimes with grim effects, as if the participants are unable to see that a given thing has many aspects.

The attitude of the scientist aiming at a balanced understanding of the universe can be summarised as follows:

Chance and necessity are for the biologist two aspects of the same causation. Necessity can be comprehended in a single instance, chance only statistically. Conscious that all plans, in fundamentals and in details, fulfil themselves according to rules, we speak of inherent purpose. Every ontogenetic process, every developmental sequence is strictly purposive, but evolutionary processes are unpredictable. The physiologist analyses causal processes and does not recognise any pre-existing barriers which would call a halt to their activities. The morphologist sees individual entities, Gestalten ordered according to their own harmony. No biologist is purely a physiologist or purely a morphologist, but always combines the two in one person. But he must keep his two sets of methods and his two languages apart, just as Bismarck, so it is said, replied to a petition which he had written, as a landowner, to himself as a Council Member, with the answer 'Refused'. In the circumscribed field of ethology the two sets of methods do in fact meet, because the field touches physiology on the one hand and psychological aspects, such as learning and memory, on the other – matters that physiology still cannot explain.

However, gaps between different fields of knowledge may be bridged, as Kant knew. Since we talk about the same thing in different languages, it is only necessary for us to learn each others' languages. We should all learn to be interpreters; only thus can we find the peaceful balance that alone is worthy of human beings and is absolutely necessary if we are to overcome the dangers that surround us.

On War and Peace in Animals and Man[1]

N. TINBERGEN

In 1935 Alexis Carrel published a bestseller, *Man – The Unknown* [1]. Today, more than thirty years later, we biologists have once more the duty to remind our fellow-men that in many respects we are still, to ourselves, unknown. It is true that we now understand a great deal of the way our bodies function. With this understanding came control: medicine.

The ignorance of ourselves which needs to be stressed today is ignorance about our behaviour – lack of understanding of the causes and effects of the function of our brains. A scientific understanding of our behaviour, leading to its control, may well be the most urgent task that faces mankind today. It is the effects of our behaviour that begin to endanger the very survival of our species and, worse, of all life on earth. By our technological achievements we have attained a mastery of our environment that is without precedent in the history of life. But these achievements are rapidly getting out of hand. The consequences of our 'rape of the earth' are now assuming critical proportions. With shortsighted recklessness we deplete the limited natural resources, including even the oxygen and nitrogen of our atmosphere [2]. And Rachel Carson's warning [3] is now being followed by those of scientists, who give us an even gloomier picture of the general pollution of air, soil, and water. This pollution is seriously threatening our health and our food supply. Refusal to curb our reproductive behaviour has led to the population explosion. And, as if all this were not enough, we are waging war on each other – men are fighting and killing men on a massive scale. It is because the effects of these behaviour

[1] Text (slightly abridged) of the author's inaugural address as Professor of Animal Behaviour, Department of Zoology, University of Oxford, 27 February 1968.

patterns, and of attitudes that determine our behaviour, have now acquired such truly lethal potentialities that I have chosen man's ignorance about his own behaviour as the subject of this paper.

What gives a student of animal behaviour the temerity to speak about problems of human behaviour? Of course the history of medicine provides the answer. We all know that medical research uses animals on a large scale. This makes sense because animals, particularly vertebrates, are, in spite of all differences, so similar to us; they are our blood relations, however distant.

But this use of zoological research for a better understanding of ourselves is, to most people, acceptable only when we have to do with those bodily functions that we look upon as parts of our physiological machinery – the functions, for instance, of our kidneys, our liver, our hormone-producing glands. The majority of people bridle as soon as it is even suggested that studies of animal behaviour could be useful for an understanding, let alone for the control, of our own behaviour. They do not want to have their own behaviour subjected to scientific scrutiny; they certainly resent being compared with animals, and these rejecting attitudes are both deep-rooted and of complex origin.

But now we are witnessing a turn in this tide of human thought. On the one hand the resistances are weakening and, on the other, a positive awareness is growing of the potentialities of a biology of behaviour. This has become quite clear from the great interest aroused by several recent books that are trying, by comparative studies of animals and man, to trace what we could call 'the animal roots of human behaviour'. As examples I select Konrad Lorenz's book *On Aggression* [4] and *The Naked Ape* by Desmond Morris [5]. Both books were bestsellers from the start. Ethologists are naturally delighted by this sign of rapid growth of interest in our science (even though the growing pains are at times a little hard to endure). But at the same time we are apprehensive, or at least I am.

We are delighted because, from the enormous sales of these and other such books, it is evident that the mental block against self-scrutiny is weakening – that there are masses of people who, so to speak, want to be shaken up.

But I am apprehensive because these books, each admirable in its own way, are being misread. Very few readers give the authors the benefit of the doubt. Far too many either accept uncritically all that the authors say, or (equally uncritically) reject it all. I believe that this is because both Lorenz and Morris emphasise our knowledge rather than our ignorance (and, in addition, present as knowledge a set of statements which are after all no more than likely guesses). In themselves brilliant, these books could stiffen, at a new level, the attitude of certainty, while what we need is a sense of doubt and wonder, and an urge to investigate, to inquire.

Now, in a way, I am going to be just as assertive as Lorenz and Morris, but what I am going to stress is how much we do not know. I shall argue that we shall have to make a major research effort. I am of course fully aware of the fact that much research is already being devoted to problems of human, and even of animal, behaviour. I know, for instance, that anthropologists, psychologists, psychiatrists, and others are approaching these problems from many angles. But I shall try to show that the research effort has so far made insufficient use of the potential of ethology. Anthropologists, for instance, are beginning to look at animals, but they restrict their work almost entirely to our nearest relatives, the apes and monkeys. Psychologists do study a larger variety of animals, but even they select mainly higher species. They also ignore certain major problems that we biologists think have to be studied. Psychiatrists, at least many of them, show a disturbing tendency to apply the *result* rather than the *methods* of ethology to man.

None of these sciences, not even their combined efforts, are as yet parts of one coherent science of behaviour. Since behaviour is a life process, its study ought to be part of the mainstream of biological research. That is why we zoologists ought to 'join the fray'. As an ethologist, I am going to try to sketch how my science could assist its sister sciences in their attempts, already well on their way, to make a united, broad-fronted, truly biological attack on the problems of behaviour.

I feel that I can co-operate best by discussing what it is in ethology that could be of use to the other behavioural sciences. What we ethologists do not want, what we consider definitely wrong, is uncritical application of our results to man. Instead, I myself at least feel that it is our method of approach, our rationale, that we can offer [6], and also a little simple common sense, and discipline.

The potential usefulness of ethology lies in the fact that, unlike other sciences of behaviour, it applies the method or 'approach' of biology to the phenomenon behaviour. It has developed a set of concepts and terms that allow us to ask:

(1) In what ways does this phenomenon (behaviour) influence the survival, the success of the animal?

(2) What makes behaviour happen at any given moment? How does its 'machinery' work?

(3) How does the behaviour machinery develop as the individual grows up?

(4) How have the behaviour systems of each species evolved until they became what they are now?

The first question, that of survival value, has to do with the effects of behaviour; the other three are, each on a different time scale, concerned with its causes.

These four questions are, as many of my fellow biologists will recognise, the major questions that biology has been pursuing for a long time. What ethology is doing could be simply described by saying that, just as biology investigates the functioning of the organs responsible for digestion, respiration, circulation, and so forth, so ethology begins now to do the same with respect to behaviour; it investigates the functioning of organs responsible for movement.

I have to make clear that in my opinion it is the comprehensive, integrated attack on all four problems that characterises ethology. I shall try to show that to ignore the questions of survival value and evolution – as, for instance, most psychologists do – is not only shortsighted but makes it impossible to arrive at an understanding of behavioural problems. Here ethology can make, in fact is already making, positive contributions.

Having stated my case for animal ethology as an essential part of the science of behaviour, I will now have to sketch how this could be done. For this I shall have to consider one concrete example, and I select aggression, the most directly lethal of our behaviours. And, for reasons that will become clear, I shall also make a short excursion into problems of education.

Let me first try to define what I mean by aggression. We all understand the term in a vague, general way, but it is, after all, no more than a catchword. In terms of actual behaviour, aggression involves approaching an opponent, and, when within reach, pushing him away, inflicting damage of some kind, or at least forcing stimuli upon him that subdue him. In this description the effect is already implicit: such behaviour tends to remove the opponent, or at least to make him change his behaviour in such a way that he no longer interferes with the attacker. The methods of attack differ from one species to another, and so do the weapons that are used, the structures that contribute to the effect.

Since I am concentrating on men fighting men, I shall confine myself to intraspecific fighting, and ignore, for instance, fighting between predators and prey. Intraspecific fighting is very common among animals. Many of them fight in two different contexts, which we can call 'offensive' and 'defensive'. Defensive fighting is often shown as a last resort by an animal that, instead of attacking, has been fleeing from an attacker. If it is cornered, it may suddenly turn round upon its enemy and 'fight with the courage of despair'.

Of the four questions I mentioned before, I shall consider that of the survival value first. Here comparison faces us right at the start with a striking paradox. On the one hand, man is akin to many species of animals in that he fights his own species. But on the other hand he is, among the thousands of species that fight, the only one in which fighting is disruptive.

In animals, intraspecific fighting is usually of distinctive advantage. In addition, all species manage as a rule to settle their disputes without killing one another; in fact, even bloodshed is rare. Man is the only species that is a mass murderer, the only misfit in his own society.

Why should this be so? For an answer, we shall have to turn to the question of causation. What makes animals and man fight their own species? And why is our species 'the odd man out'?

For a fruitful discussion of this question of causation I shall first have to discuss what exactly we mean when we ask it.

I have already indicated that when thinking of causation we have to distinguish between three subquestions, and that these three differ from one another in the stretch of time that is considered. We ask, first: Given an adult animal that fights now and then, what makes each outburst of fighting happen? The time scale in which we consider these recurrent events is usually one of seconds, or minutes. To use an analogy, this subquestion compares with asking what makes a car start or stop each time we use it.

But in asking this same general question of causation ('What makes an animal fight?') we may also be referring to a longer period of time; we may mean 'How has the animal, as it grew up, developed this behaviour?' This compares roughly with asking how a car has been constructed in the factory. The distinction between these two subquestions remains useful even though we know that many animals continue their development (much slowed down) even after they have attained adulthood. For instance, they may still continue to learn.

Finally, in biology, as in technology, we can extend this time scale even more, and ask: How have the animal species which we observe today – and which we know have evolved from ancestors that were different – how have they acquired their particular behaviour systems during this evolution? Unfortunately, while we know the evolution of cars because they evolved so quickly and have been so fully recorded, the behaviour of extinct animals cannot be observed, and has to be reconstructed by indirect methods.

I shall try to justify the claim I made earlier, and show how all these four questions – that of behaviour's survival value and the three subquestions of causation – have to enter into the argument if we are to understand the biology of aggression.

Let us first consider the short-term causation; the mechanism of fighting. What makes us fight at any one moment? Lorenz argues in his book that, in animals and in man, there is an internal urge to attack. An individual does not simply wait to be provoked, but, if actual attack has not been possible for some time, this urge to fight builds up until the individual actively seeks the opportunity to indulge in fighting. Aggression, Lorenz claims, can be spontaneous.

But this view has not gone unchallenged. For instance, R. A. Hinde has written a thorough criticism [7], based on recent work on aggression in animals, in which he writes that Lorenz's 'arguments for the spontaneity of aggression do not bear examination' and that 'the contrary view, expressed in nearly every textbook of comparative psychology ...' is that fighting 'derives principally from the situation'; and even more explicitly: 'There is no need to postulate causes that are purely internal to the aggressor' [7, p. 303]. At first glance it would seem as if Lorenz and Hinde disagree profoundly. I have read and reread both authors, and it is to me perfectly clear that loose statements and misunderstandings on both sides have made it appear that there is disagreement where in fact there is something very near to a common opinion. It seems to me that the differences between the two authors lie mainly in the different ways they look at internal and external variables. This in turn seems due to differences of a semantic nature. Lorenz uses the unfortunate term 'the spontaneity of aggression'. Hinde takes this to mean that external stimuli are in Lorenz's view not necessary at all to make an animal fight. But here he misrepresents Lorenz, for nowhere does Lorenz claim that the internal urge ever makes an animal fight 'in vacuo'; somebody or something is attacked. This misunderstanding makes Hinde feel that he has refuted Lorenz's views by saying that 'fighting derives principally from the situation'. But both authors are fully aware of the fact that fighting is started by a number of variables, of which some are internal and some external. What both authors know, and what cannot be doubted, is that fighting behaviour is not like the simple slot machine that produces one platform ticket every time one threepenny bit is inserted. To mention one animal example: a male stickleback does not always show the full fighting behaviour in response to an approaching standard opponent; its response varies from none at all to the optimal stimulus on some occasions, to full attack on even a crude dummy at other times. This means that its internal state varies, and in this particular case we know from the work of Hoar [8] that the level of the male sex hormone is an important variable.

Another source of misunderstanding seems to have to do with the stretch of time that the two authors are taking into account. Lorenz undoubtedly thinks of the causes of an outburst of fighting in terms of seconds, or hours – perhaps days. Hinde seems to think of events which may have happened further back in time; an event which is at any particular moment 'internal' may well in its turn have been influenced previously by external agents. In our stickleback example, the level of male sex hormone is influenced by external agents such as the length of the daily exposure to light over a period of a month or so [9]. Or, less far back in time, its readiness to attack may have been influenced by some experience gained, say, half an hour before the fight.

I have spent much time here on what would seem to be a perfectly simple issue: the very first step in the analysis of the short-term causation, which is to distinguish at any given moment between variables within the animal and variables in the environment. It is of course important for our further understanding to unravel the complex interactions between these two worlds, and in particular the physiology of aggressive behaviour. A great deal is being discovered about this, but for my present issue there is no use discussing it as long as even the first step in the analysis has not led to a clearly expressed and generally accepted conclusion. We must remember that we are at the moment concerned with the human problem: 'What makes men attack each other?' And for this problem the answer to the first stage of our question is of prime importance: Is our readiness to start an attack constant or not? If it were – if our aggressive behaviour were the outcome of an apparatus with the properties of the slot machine – all we would have to do would be to control the external situation: to stop providing threepenny bits. But since our readiness to start an attack is variable, further studies of both the external and the internal variables are vital to such issues as: Can we reduce fighting by lowering the population density, or by withholding provocative stimuli? Can we do so by changing the hormone balance or other physiological variables? Can we perhaps in addition control our development in such a way as to change the dependence on internal and external factors in adult man? However, before discussing development, I must first return to the fact that I have mentioned before, namely, that man is, among the thousands of other species that fight, the only mass murderer. How do animals in their intra-specific disputes avoid bloodshed?

The clue to this problem is to recognise the simple fact that aggression in animals rarely occurs in pure form; it is only one of two components of an adaptive system. This is most clearly seen in territorial behaviour, although it is also true of most other types of hostile behaviour. Members of territorial species divide, among themselves, the available living space and opportunities by each individual defending its home range against competitors. Now in this system of parcelling our living space, avoidance plays as important a part as attack. Put very briefly, animals of territorial species, once they have settled on a territory, attack intruders, but an animal that is still searching for a suitable territory or finds itself outside its home range withdraws when it meets with an already established owner. In terms of function, once you have taken possession of a territory, it pays to drive off competitors; but when you are still looking for a territory (or meet your neighbour at your common boundary), your chances of success are improved by avoiding such established owners. The ruthless fighter who 'knows no fear' does not get very far. For an understanding of what follows, this fact, that hostile clashes are controlled by what we could call the 'attack-avoidance system', is essential.

When neighbouring territory owners meet near their common boundary, both attack behaviour and withdrawal behaviour are elicited in both animals; each of the two is in a state of motivational conflict. We know a great deal about the variety of movements that appear when these two conflicting, incompatible behaviours are elicited. Many of these expressions of a motivational conflict have, in the course of evolution, acquired signal function; in colloquial language, they signal 'Keep out!' We deduce this from the fact that opponents respond to them in an appropriate way: instead of proceeding to intrude, which would require the use of force, trespassers withdraw, and neighbours are contained by each other. This is how such animals have managed to have all the advantages of their hostile behaviour without the disadvantages: they divide their living space in a bloodless way by using as distance-keeping devices these conflict movements ('threat') rather than actual fighting.

In order to see our wars in their correct biological perspective one more comparison with animals is useful. So far I have discussed animal species that defend individual or at best pair territories. But there are also animals which possess and defend territories belonging to a group, or a clan [10].

Now it is an essential aspect of group territorialism that the members of a group unite when in hostile confrontation with another group that approaches, or crosses into their feeding territory. The uniting and the aggression are equally important. It is essential to realise that group territorialism does not exclude hostile relations on lower levels when the group is on its own. For instance, within a group there is often a peck order. And within the group there may be individual or pair territories. But frictions due to these relationships fade away during a clash between groups. This temporary elimination is done by means of so-called appeasement and reassurance signals. They indicate 'I am a friend', and so diminish the risk that, in the general flare-up of anger, any animal 'takes it out' on a fellow-member of the same group [11]. Clans meet clans as units, and each individual in an intergroup clash, while united with its fellow-members, is (as in interindividual clashes) torn between attack and withdrawal, and postures and shouts rather than attacks.

We must now examine the hypothesis (which I consider the most likely one) that man still carries with him the animal heritage of group territoriality. This is a question concerning man's evolutionary origin, and here we are, by the very nature of the subject, forced to speculate. Because I am going to say something about the behaviour of our ancestors of, say, one hundred thousand years ago, I have to discuss briefly a matter of method-ology. It is known to all biologists (but unfortunately unknown to most psychologists) that comparison of present-day species can give us a deep insight, with a probability closely approaching certainty, into the evolutionary history of animal species. Even where fossil evidence is lacking, this comparative method alone can do this. It has to be stressed that this comparison is a highly sophisticated method, and not merely a matter of saying that species A is different from species B [12]. The basic procedure is this. We interpret differences between really allied species as the result of adaptive divergent evolution from common stock, and we interpret similarities between non-allied species as adaptive convergencies to similar ways of life. By studying the adaptive functions of species characteristics we understand how natural selection can have produced both these divergencies and convergencies. To mention one striking example: even if we had no fossil evidence, we could, by this method alone, recognise whales for what they are – mammals that have returned to the water, and, in doing so, have developed some similarities to fish. This special type of comparison, which has been applied so successfully by students of the structure of animals, has now also been used, and with equal success, in several studies of animal behaviour. Two approaches have been applied. One is to see in what respects species of very different origin have convergently adapted to a similar way of life. Von Haartman [13] has applied this to a study of birds of many types that nest in holes – an anti-predator safety device. All such hole-nesters centre their terri-torial fighting on a suitable nest hole. Their courtship consists of luring a female to this hole (often with the use of bright colour patterns). Their young gape when a general darkening signals the arrival of the parent. All but the most recently adapted species lay uniformly coloured, white or light blue eggs that can easily be seen by the parent.

An example of adaptive divergence has been studied by Cullen [14]. Among all the gulls, the kittiwake is unique in that it nests on very narrow ledges on sheer cliffs. Over twenty peculiarities of this species have been recognised by Mrs Cullen as vital adaptations to this particular habitat.

These and several similar studies [15] demonstrate how comparison reveals, in each species, systems of interrelated, and very intricate adaptive features. In this work, speculation is now being followed by careful experimental checking. It would be tempting to elaborate on this, but I must return to our own unfortunate species.

Now, when we include the 'Naked Ape' in our comparative studies, it becomes likely (as has been recently worked out in great detail by Morris) that man is a 'social Ape who has turned carnivore' [16]. On the one hand he is a social primate; on the other, he has developed similarities to wolves, lions, and hyenas. In our present context one thing seems to stand out clearly, a conclusion that seems to me of paramount importance to all of us, and yet has not yet been fully accepted as such. As a social, hunting primate, man must originally have been organised on the principle of group territories.

Ethologists tend to believe that we still carry with us a number of behavioural characteristics of our animal ancestors, which cannot be eliminated by different ways of upbringing, and that our group territorialism is one of those ancestral characters. I shall discuss the problem of the modifiability of our behaviour later, but it is useful to point out here that even if our behaviour were much more modifiable than Lorenz maintains, our cultural evolution, which resulted in the parcelling-out of our living space on lines of tribal, national, and now even 'bloc' areas, would, if anything, have tended to enhance group territorialism.

I put so much emphasis on this issue of group territorialism because most writers who have tried to apply ethology to man have done this in the wrong way. They have made the mistake, to which I objected before, of uncritically extrapolating the results of animal studies to man. They try to explain man's behaviour by using facts that are valid only of some of the animals we studied. And, as ethologists keep stressing, no two species behave alike. Therefore, instead of taking this easy way out, we ought to study man in his own right. And I repeat that the message of the ethologists is that the methods, rather than the results, of ethology should be used for such a study.

Now, the notion of territory was developed by zoologists [to be precise, by ornithologists, 17], and because individual and pair territories are found in so many more species than group territories (which are particularly rare among birds), most animal studies were concerned with such individual and pair territories. Now such low-level territories do occur in man, as does another form of hostile behaviour, the peck order. But the problems created by such low-level frictions are not serious; they can, within a community, be kept in check by the apparatus of law and order; peace within national boundaries can be enforced. In order to understand what makes us go to war, we have to recognise that man behaves very much like a group-territorial species. We too unite in the face of an outside danger to the group; we 'forget our differences'. We too have threat gestures, for instance, angry facial expressions. And all of us use reassurance and appeasement signals, such as a friendly smile. And (unlike speech) these are universally understood; they are crosscultural; they are species-specific. And, incidentally, even within a group sharing a common language, they are often more reliable guides to a man's intentions than speech, for speech (as we know now) rarely reflects our true motives, but our facial expressions often 'give us away'.

If I may digress for a moment: it is humiliating to us ethologists that many non-scientists, particularly novelists and actors, intuitively understand our sign language much better than we scientists ourselves do. Worse, there is a category of human beings who understand intuitively more about the causation of our aggressive behaviour: the great demagogues. They have applied this knowledge in order to control our behaviour in the most clever ways, and often for the most evil purposes. For instance, Hitler (who had modern mass communication at his disposal, which allowed him to inflame a whole nation) played on both fighting tendencies. The 'defensive' fighting was whipped up by his passionate statements about 'living space', 'encirclement', Jewry, and Freemasonry as threatening powers which made the Germans feel 'cornered'. The 'attack fighting' was similarly set ablaze by playing the myth of the Herrenvolk. We must make sure that mankind has learned its lesson and will never forget how disastrous the joint effects have been – if only one of the major nations were led now by a man like Hitler, life on earth would be wiped out.

I have argued my case for concentrating on studies of group territoriality rather than on other types of aggression. I must now return, in this context, to the problem of man the mass murderer. Why don't we settle even our international disputes by the relatively harmless, animal method of threat? Why have we become unhinged so that so often our attack erupts without being kept in check by fear? It is not that we have no fear, nor that we have no other inhibitions against killing. This problem has to be considered first of all in the general context of the consequences of man having embarked on a new type of evolution.

Man has the ability, unparalleled in scale in the animal kingdom, of passing on his experiences from one generation to the next. By this accumulative and exponentially growing process, which we call cultural evolution, he has been able to change his environment progressively out of all recognition. And this includes the social environment. This new type of evolution proceeds at an incomparably faster pace than genetic evolution. Genetically we have not evolved very strikingly since Cro-Magnon man, but culturally we have changed beyond recognition, and are changing at an ever-increasing rate. It is of course true that we are highly adjustable individually, and so could hope to keep pace with these changes. But I am not alone in believing that this behavioural adjustability, like all types of modifiability, has its limits. These limits are imposed upon us by our hereditary constitution, a constitution which can only change with the far slower speed of genetic evolution. There are good grounds for the conclusion that man's limited behavioural adjustability has been outpaced by the culturally determined changes in his social environment, and that this is why man is now a misfit in his own society.

We can now, at last, return to the problem of war, of uninhibited mass killing. It seems quite clear that our cultural evolution is at the root of the trouble. It is our cultural evolution that has caused the population explosion. In a nutshell, medical science, aiming at the reduction of suffering, has, in doing so, prolonged life for many individuals as well – prolonged it to well beyond the point at which they produce offspring. Unlike the situation in any wild species, recruitment to the human population consistently surpasses losses through mortality. Agricultural and technical know-how have enabled us to grow food and to exploit other natural resources to such an extent that we can still feed (though only just) the enormous numbers of human beings on our crowded planet. The result is that we now live at a far higher density than that in which genetic evolution has moulded our species. This, together with long-distance communication, leads to far more frequent, in fact to continuous, intergroup contacts, and so to continuous external provocation of aggression. Yet this alone would not explain our increased tendency to kill each other; it would merely lead to continuous threat behaviour.

The upsetting of the balance between aggression and fear (and this is what causes war) is due to at least three other consequences of cultural evolution. It is an old cultural phenomenon that warriors are both brainwashed and bullied into all-out fighting. They are brainwashed into believing that fleeing – originally, as we have seen, an adaptive type of behaviour – is despicable, 'cowardly'. This seems to me due to the fact that man, accepting that in moral issues death might be preferable to fleeing, has falsely applied the moral concept of 'cowardice' to matters of mere practical importance – to the dividing of living space. The fact that our soldiers are also bullied into all-out fighting (by penalising fleeing in battle) is too well known to deserve elaboration.

Another cultural excess is our ability to make and use killing tools, especially long-range weapons. These make killing easy, not only because a spear or a club inflicts, with the same effort, so much more damage than a fist, but also, and mainly, because the use of long-range weapons prevents the victim from reaching his attacker with his appeasement, reassurance, and distress signals. Very few aircrews who are willing, indeed eager, to drop their bombs 'on target' would be willing to strangle, stab, or burn children (or, for that matter, adults) with their own hands; they would stop short of killing, in response to the appeasement and distress signals of their opponents.

These three factors alone would be sufficient to explain how we have become such unhinged killers. But I have to stress once more that all this, however convincing it may seem, must still be studied more thoroughly.

There is a frightening and ironical paradox in this conclusion: that the human brain, the finest life-preserving device created by evolution, has made our species so successful in mastering the outside world that it suddenly finds itself taken off guard. One could say that our cortex and our brainstem (our 'reason' and our 'instincts') are at loggerheads. Together they have created a new social environment in which, rather than ensuring our survival, they are about to do the opposite. The brain finds itself seriously threatened by an enemy of its own making. It is its own enemy. We simply have to understand this enemy.

I must now leave the question of the moment-to-moment control of fighting, and, looking further back in time, turn to the development of aggressive behaviour in the growing individual. Again we will start from the human problem. This, in the present context, is whether it is within our power to control development in such a way that we reduce or eliminate fighting among adults. Can or cannot education in the widest sense produce nonaggressive men?

The first step in the consideration of this problem is again to distinguish between external and internal influences, but now we must apply this to the growth, the changing, of the behavioural machinery during the individual's development. Here again the way in which we phrase our questions and our conclusions is of the utmost importance.

In order to discuss this issue fruitfully, I have to start once more by considering it in a wider context, which is now that of the 'nature-nurture' problem with respect to behaviour in general. This has been discussed more fully by Lorenz in his book *Evolution and Modification of Behaviour* [18]; for a discussion of the environmentalist point of view I refer to the various works of Schneirla [see 19].

Lorenz tends to classify behaviour types into innate and acquired or learned behaviour. Schneirla rejects this dichotomy into two classes of behaviour. He stresses that the developmental process, of behaviour as well as of other functions, should be considered, and also that this development forms a highly complicated series of interactions between the growing organism and its environment. I have gradually become convinced that the clue to this difference in approach is to be found in a difference in aims between the two authors. Lorenz claims that 'we are justified in leaving, at least for the time being, to the care of the experimental embryologists all those questions which are concerned with the chains of physiological causation leading from the genome to the development of . . . neurosensory structures' [18, p. 43]. In other words, he deliberately refrains from starting his analysis of development prior to the stage at which a fully co-ordinated behaviour is performed for the first time. If one in this way restricts one's studies to the later stages of development, then a classification in 'innate' and 'learned' behaviour, or behaviour components, can be considered quite justified. And there was a time, some thirty years ago, when the almost grotesquely environmentalist bias of psychology made it imperative for ethologists to stress the extent to which behaviour patterns could appear in perfect or near-perfect form without the aid of anything that could be properly called learning. But I now agree (however belatedly) with Schneirla that we must extend our interest to earlier stages of development and embark on a full programme of experimental embryology of behaviour. When we do this, we discover that interactions with the environment can indeed occur at early stages. These interactions may concern small components of the total machinery of a fully functional behaviour pattern, and many of them cannot possibly be called learning. But they are interactions with the environment, and must be taken into account if we follow in the footsteps of the experimental embryologists, and extend our field of interest to the entire sequence of events which lead from the blueprints contained in the zygote to the fully functioning, behaving animal.

We simply have to do this if we want an answer to the question to what extent the development of behaviour can be influenced from the outside.

When we follow this procedure the rigid distinction between 'innate' or unmodifiable and 'acquired' or modifiable behaviour patterns becomes far less sharp. This is owing to the discovery, on the one hand, that 'innate' patterns may contain elements that at an early stage developed in interaction with the environment, and, on the other hand, that learning is, from step to step, limited by internally imposed restrictions.

To illustrate the first point, I take the development of the sensory cells in the retina of the eye. Knoll has shown [20] that the rods in the eyes of tadpoles cannot function properly unless they have first been exposed to light. This means that, although any visually guided response of a tadpole may well, in its integrated form, be 'innate' in Lorenz's sense, it is so only in the sense of 'non-learned', not in that of 'having grown without interaction with the environment'. Now it has been shown by Cullen [21] that male sticklebacks reared from the egg in complete isolation from other animals will, when adult, show full fighting behaviour to other males and courtship behaviour to females when faced with them for the first time in their lives. This is admittedly an important fact, demonstrating that the various recognised forms of learning do not enter into the programming of these integrated patterns. This is a demonstration of what Lorenz calls an 'innate response'. But it does not exclude the possibility that parts of the machinery so employed may, at an earlier stage, have been influenced by the environment, as in the case of the tadpoles.

Second, there are also behaviour patterns which do appear in the inexperienced animal, but in an incomplete form, and which require additional development through learning. Thorpe has analysed a clear example of this: when young male chaffinches reared alone begin to produce their song for the first time, they utter a very imperfect warble; this develops into the full song only if, at a certain sensitive stage, the young birds have heard the full song of an adult male [22].

By far the most interesting aspect of such intermediates

between innate and acquired behaviour is the fact that learning is not indiscriminate, but is guided by a certain selectiveness on the part of the animal. This fact has been dimly recognised long ago; the early ethologists have often pointed out that different, even closely related, species learn different things even when developing the same behaviour patterns. This has been emphasized by Lorenz's use of the term 'innate teaching mechanism'. Other authors use the word 'template' in the same context. The best example I know is once more taken from the development of song in certain birds. As I have mentioned, the males of some birds acquire their full song by changing their basic repertoire to resemble the song of adults, which they have to hear during a special sensitive period some months before they sing themselves. It is in this sensitive period that they acquire, without as yet producing the song, the knowledge of 'what the song ought to be like'. In technical terms, the birds form a *Sollwert* [23] (literally, 'should-value', an ideal) for the feedback they receive when they hear their own first attempts. Experiments have shown [24] that such birds, when they start to sing, do three things: they listen to what they produce; they notice the difference between this feedback and the ideal song; and they correct their next performance.

This example, while demonstrating an internal teaching mechanism, shows, at the same time, that Lorenz made his concept too narrow when he coined the term 'innate teaching mechanism'. The birds have developed a teaching mechanism, but while it is true that it is internal, it is not innate; the birds have acquired it by listening to their father's song.

These examples show that if behaviour studies are to catch up with experimental embryology our aims, our concepts, and our terms must be continually revised.

Before returning to aggression, I should like to elaborate a little further on general aspects of behaviour development, because this will enable me to show the value of animal studies in another context, that of education.

Comparative studies, of different animal species, of different behaviour patterns, and of different stages of development, begin to suggest that wherever learning takes a hand in development, it is guided by such *Sollwerte* or templates for the proper feedback, the feedback that reinforces. And it becomes clear that these various *Sollwerte* are of a bewildering variety. In human education one aspect of this has been emphasised in particular, and even applied in the use of teaching machines: the requirement that the reward, in order to have maximum effect, must be immediate. Skinner has stressed this so much because in our own teaching we have imposed an unnatural delay between, say, taking in homework, and giving the pupil his reward in the form of a mark. But we can learn more from animal studies than the need for immediacy of reward. The type of reward is also of great importance, and this may vary from task to task, from stage to stage, from occasion to occasion; the awards may be of almost infinite variety.

Here I have to discuss briefly a behaviour of which I have so far been unable to find the equivalent in the development of structure. This is exploratory behaviour. By this we mean a kind of behaviour in which the animal sets out to acquire as much information about an object or a situation as it can possibly get. The behaviour is intricately adapted to this end, and it terminates when the information has been stored, when the animal has incorporated it in its learned knowledge. This exploration (subjectively we speak of 'curiosity') is not confined to the acquisition of information about the external world alone; at least mammals explore their own movements a great deal, and in this way 'master new skills'. Again, in this exploratory behaviour, *Sollwerte* of expected, 'hoped-for' feedbacks play their part.

Without going into more detail, we can characterise the picture we begin to get of the development of behaviour as a series, or rather a web, of events, starting with innate programming instructions contained in the zygote, which straightaway begin to interact with the environment; this interaction may be discontinuous, in that periods of predominantly internal development alternate with periods of interaction, or sensitive periods. The interaction is enhanced by active exploration; it is steered by selective *Sollwerte* of great variety; and stage by stage this process ramifies; level upon level of ever-increasing complexity is being incorporated into the programming.

Apply what we have heard for a moment to playing children (I do not, of course, distinguish sharply between 'play' and 'learning'). At a certain age a child begins to use, say, building blocks. It will at first manipulate them in various ways, one at a time. Each way of manipulating acts as exploratory behaviour: the child learns what a block looks, feels, tastes like, and so forth, and also how to put it down so that it stands stably.

Each of these stages 'peters out' when the child knows what it wanted to find out. But as the development proceeds, a new level of exploration is added: the child discovers that it can put one block on top of the other; it constructs. The new discovery leads to repetition and variation, for each child develops, at some stage, a desire and a set of *Sollwerte* for such effects of construction, and acts out to the full this new level of exploratory behaviour. In addition, already at this stage the *Sollwert* or ideal does not merely contain what the blocks do, but also what, for instance, the mother does; her approval, her shared enjoyment, is also of great importance. Just as an exploring animal, the child builds a kind of inverted pyramid of experience, built of layers, each set off by a new wave of exploration and each directed by new sets of *Sollwerte*, and so its development 'snowballs'. All these phases may well have more or less limited sensitive periods, which determine when the fullest effect can be obtained, and when the child is ready for the next step. More important still, if the opportunity for the next stage is offered either too early or too late, development may be damaged, including the development of motivational and emotional attitudes.

Of course gifted teachers of many generations have known all these things [25] or some of them, but the glimpses of insight have not been fully and scientifically systematised. In human education, this would of course involve experimentation. This need not worry us too much, because in our search for better educational procedures we are in effect experimenting on our children all the time. Also, children are fortunately incredibly resilient, and most grow up into pretty viable adults in spite of our fumbling educational efforts. Yet there is, of course, a limit to what we will allow ourselves, and this, I should like to emphasise, is where animal studies may well become even more important than they are already.

Returning now to the development of animal and human aggression, I hope to have made at least several things clear: that behaviour development is a very complex phenomenon indeed; that we have only begun to analyse it in animals; that with respect to man we are, if anything, behind in comparison with animal studies; and that I cannot do otherwise than repeat what I said in the beginning: a major research effort is required. In this effort animal studies can help, but we are still very far from drawing very definite conclusions with regard to our question: To what extent shall we be able to render man less aggressive through manipulation of the environment, that is, by educational measures?

In such a situation personal opinions naturally vary a great deal. I do not hesitate to give as my personal opinion that Lorenz's book *On Aggression*, in spite of certain reservations I have about it and in spite of the many possibilities of misunderstandings due to the lack of a common language among students of behaviour, must be taken more seriously as a positive contribution to our problem than many critics have done. Lorenz is, in my opinion, right in claiming that elimination, through education, of the internal urge to fight will turn out to be very difficult, if not impossible.

Everything I have said so far seems to me to allow for only one conclusion. Apart from doing our utmost to return to a reasonable population density, apart from stopping the progressive depletion and pollution of our habitat, we must pursue the biological study of animal behaviour for clarifying problems of human behaviour of such magnitude as that of our aggression, and of education.

But research takes a long time, and we must remember that there are experts who forecast worldwide famine ten to twenty years from now; and that we have enough weapons to wipe out all human life on earth. Whatever the causation of our aggression, the simple fact is that for the time being we are saddled with it. This means that there is a crying need for a crash programme, for finding ways and means for keeping our intergroup aggression in check. This is of course in practice infinitely more difficult than controlling our intranational frictions; we have as yet not got a truly international police force. But there is hope for avoiding all-out war because, for the first time in history, we are afraid of killing ourselves by the lethal radiation effects even of bombs that we could drop in the enemy's territory. Our politicians know this. And as long as there is this hope, there is every reason to try and learn what we can from animal studies. Here again they can be of help. We have already seen that animal opponents meeting in a hostile clash avoid bloodshed by using the expressions of their motivational conflicts as intimidating signals. Ethologists have studied such conflict movements in some detail [26], and have found that they are of a variety of types. The most instructive of these is the redirected attack; instead of attacking the provoking, yet dreaded, opponent, animals often attack something else, often even an inanimate object. We ourselves bang the table with our fists. Redirection includes something like sublimation, a term attaching a value judgement to the redirection. As a species with group territories, humans, like hyenas, unite when meeting a common enemy. We do already sublimate our group aggression. The Dutch feel united in their fight against the sea. Scientists do attack their problems together. The space programme – surely a mainly military effort – is an up-to-date example. I would not like to claim, as Lorenz does in his book, that redirected attack exhausts the aggressive urge. We know from soccer matches and from animal work how aggressive behaviour has two simultaneous, but opposite effects: a waning effect, and one of self-inflammation, of mass hysteria, such as recently seen in Cairo. Of these two the inflammatory effect often wins. But if aggression were used successfully as the motive force behind non-killing and even useful activities, self-stimulation need not be a danger; in our short-term cure we are not aiming at the elimination of aggressiveness, but at 'taking the sting out of it'.

Of all sublimated activities, scientific research would seem to offer the best opportunities for deflecting and sublimating our aggression. And, once we recognise that it is the disrupted relation between our own behaviour and our environment that forms our most deadly enemy, what could be better than uniting, at the front or behind the lines, in the scientific attack on our own behavioural problems?

I stress 'behind the lines'. The whole population should be made to feel that it participates in the struggle. This is why scientists will always have the duty to inform their fellow-men of what they are doing, of the relevance and the importance of their work. And this is not only a duty, it can give intense satisfaction.

I have come full circle. For both the long-term and the short-term remedies at least we scientists will have to sublimate our aggression into an all-out attack on the enemy within. For this the enemy must be recognised for what it is: our unknown selves, or, deeper down, our refusal to admit that man is, to himself, unknown.

REFERENCES

1. A. Carrel, *L'Homme, cet Inconnu* (Librairie Plon, Paris, 1935).
2. AAAS Annual Meeting, 1967 (see *New Scientist* 37, 5, 1968).
3. R. Carson, *Silent Spring* (Houghton Mifflin, Boston, 1962).
4. K. Lorenz, *On Aggression* (Methuen, London, 1966).
5. D. Morris, *The Naked Ape* (Jonathan Cape, London, 1967).
6. N. Tinbergen, *Zeitschrift für Tierpsychologie* 20, 410 (1964).
7. R. A. Hinde, *New Society* 9, 302 (1967).
8. W. S. Hoar, *Animal Behaviour* 10, 247 (1962).
9. B. Baggerman, in *Symposium of the Society for Experimental Biology* 20, 427 (1965).
10. H. Kruuk, *New Scientist* 30, 849 (1966).
11. Tinbergen, *Zeitschrift für Tierpsychologie* 16, 651 (1959); *Zoologische Mededelingen* 39, 209 (1964).
12. Tinbergen, *Behaviour* 15, 1–70 (1959).
13. L. von Haartman, *Evolution* 11, 339 (1957).
14. E. Cullen, *Ibis* 99, 275 (1957).
15. J. H. Crook, *Symposium of the Zoological Society of London* 14, 181 (1965).
16. D. Freeman, *Institute of Biology Symposium* 13, 109 (1964); Morris, Ed., *Primate Ethology* (Weidenfeld and Nicolson, London, 1967).

17. H. E. Howard, *Territory in Bird Life* (Murray, London, 1920); R. A. Hinde *et al.*, *Ibis* 98, 340–530 (1956).

18. Lorenz, *Evolution and Modification of Behaviour* (Methuen, London, 1966).

19. T. C. Schneirla, *Quarterly Review of Biology* 41, 283 (1966).

20. M. D. Knoll, *Zeitschrift für Vergleichende Physiologie* 38, 219 (1956).

21. Cullen, *Final Rept. Contr. AF 61 (052)–29*, USAFRDC, 1–23 (1961).

22. W. H. Thorpe, *Bird-Song* (Cambridge University Press, New York, 1961).

23. E. von Holst and H. Mittelstaedt, *Naturwissenschaften* 37, 464 (1950).

24. M. Konishi, *Zeitschrift für Tierpsychologie* 22, 770 (1965); F. Nottebohm, *Proceedings of the 14th International Ornithological Congress* 265–280 (1967).

25. E. M. Standing, *Maria Montessori* (New American Library, New York, 1962).

26. Tinbergen, in *The Pathology and Treatment of Sexual Deviation*, I. Rosen, Ed. (Oxford University Press, London, 1964), pp. 3–23; N. B. Jones, *Wildfowl Trust 11th Annual Report*, 46–52 (1960); P. Sevenster, *Behaviour, Supplement* 9, 1–170 (1961); F. Rowell, *Animal Behaviour* 9, 38 (1961),

Notes on Contributors

Professor Dr HANSJOCHEM AUTRUM, born in 1907, is an internationally known expert in sensory physiology. He is the Principal of the Zoological Institute of the University of Munich, where he lectures and conducts research.

Professor Dr SVEN DIJKGRAAF, born in 1908, is Principal of the Laboratory of Comparative Physiology at the University of Utrecht. He is well known as a specialist in ethology.

HEINZ FRIEDRICH, born in 1922, is Managing Director of Deutscher Taschenbuch Verlag, Munich. He was previously Editor for Science and Literature at the Hessischer Rundfunk, Frankfurt.

Professor Dr KARL VON FRISCH, born in 1886, preceded Professor Autrum as Principal of the Zoological Institute at the University of Munich. He discovered 'bee language'. Apart from scientific works, he has written the popular book *Unsere Hausgenossen* (Our Household Friends) and *Du und das Leben* (You and Life).

Professor Dr BERNHARD GRZIMEK, born in 1909, is the Director of the Zoological Gardens, Frankfurt a.M. He also teaches at the University of Giessen. He has published a number of books about his experiences with animals, in particular about his expeditions in African Game Reserves (*Sergengeti Shall not Die*). Under his guidance *Grzimeks Tierleben* (Grzimek's Life of the Animals), a thirteen-volume history of animals, is now being compiled.

Professor Dr ERICH VON HOLST, born in 1908, up till his death in 1962 co-directed with Konrad Lorenz the Max Planck Institute for Behavioural Physiology in Seewiesen. His brilliant researches into the physiology of the central nervous system exerted a decisive influence not only in zoology but also in cybernetics. His collected papers are at present being translated into English under the title *The Behavioural Physiology of Animals and Men*.

Professor Dr OTTO KOEHLER, born in 1889, Emeritus Professor of Zoology at the University of Freiburg in Breisgau, edited until recently, together with Konrad Lorenz, *Zeitschrift für Tierpsychologie* (Journal of Animal Psychology). His work on non-verbal thinking in animals was a decisive factor in linking animal and human psychology.

Professor Dr KONRAD LORENZ, born in 1903, has been a director of the Max Planck Institute for Behavioural Physiology in Seewiesen since its foundation. He is considered to be the founder of modern ethology. Konrad Lorenz is widely known both through his two popular books *King Solomon's Ring* and *On Aggression* and his collection of scientific papers *Studies in Animal and Human Behaviour*.

Professor N. TINBERGEN, born in 1907, is Professor of Animal Behaviour in the Department of Zoology at Oxford University. He is particularly distinguished for his researches into the social interactions of animals and studies of adaptation for survival under natural conditions. His popular books include *The Herring Gull's World* and *Animal Tracks*, while two of his more technical books – *The Study of Instinct* and *The Social Behaviour of Animals* – have become standard university texts.

for each one of us in particular, provided that we have the proper attachment for the author of all, not only as the Architect and the efficient cause of our being, but also as our Lord and the Final Cause, who ought to be the whole goal of our will, and who alone can make us happy.

9C